Kit Wilson, RN

Treading Water

Beth E. Heinzeroth White

ISBN number:
(paperback) 978-1-7359347-2-3
(digital/e-book) 978-1-7359347-0

This book is a work of fiction. Any resemblance to locations or persons, living or dead, is a coincidence. The story is purely from my imagination and not a reflection of any actual events. This book is not meant to be a medical or nursing reference. The author has made every effort to ensure that the information was correct and that referenced online links were active on the publication date.

First printing edition 2022
BHW Publishing, LLC
Permissions address:
bethewhite@betheheinzerothwhite.com

This book is dedicated to:

- David Nelson White, who believed in me.

- The Kit Wilson, RN books recognize, and hope to accurately reflect, the work of the millions of nurses who, every day and night, willingly negotiate our baffling health care system to provide compassionate, knowledgeable care to patients and families. You are the scaffolding that supports health care. Without you, hospitals would have no reason to exist.

Other Books
by

Beth E. Heinzeroth White

Kit Wilson, RN: First Year Nurse, *BHW Publishing, LLC 2022*

With Patricia Ringos Beach:
In the Shadows: How to Help Your Seriously Ill Adult Child, *Hygeia Media 2013*
Caps, Capes and Caring: The Legacy of Diploma Nursing Schools in Toledo, *University of Toledo Press 2018*

Contents

Acknowledgments... vii
Introduction ix

Chapter One 1
Chapter Two 5
Chapter Three..9
Chapter Four 13
Chapter Five..19
Chapter Six...23
Chapter Seven 27
Chapter Eight 31
Chapter Nine 35
Chapter Ten 41
Chapter Eleven..45
Chapter Twelve 49
Chapter Thirteen 55
Chapter Fourteen..61
Chapter Fifteen...63
Chapter Sixteen...67
Chapter Seventeen 71
Chapter Eighteen..75
Chapter Nineteen 81
Chapter Twenty 87
Chapter Twenty-One 91
Chapter Twenty-Two..97
Chapter Twenty-Three 101
Chapter Twenty-Four 111

Chapter Twenty-Five..115
Chapter Twenty-Six 121
Chapter Twenty-Seven...127
Chapter Twenty-Eight..129
Chapter Twenty-Nine 139
Chapter Thirty...143
Chapter Thirty-One...153
Chapter Thirty-Two...161
Chapter Thirty-Three...165
Chapter Thirty-Four 169
Chapter Thirty-Five...171
Chapter Thirty-Six 175
Chapter Thirty-Seven...179
Chapter Thirty-Eight 185
Chapter Thirty-Nine..189
Chapter Forty 193

Thank you for reading Kit Wilson, RN: Treading Water. 197
References and Credit Notes:..199
About the Author..203

Acknowledgments

- Patricia Ringos Beach, Kevin Hayes, Maureen Knowles, Maria Nowicki, and Judy Harris Szor, who reviewed multiple revisions to this book are acknowledged with gratitude. It's not possible to explain how much I depend on you to clarify my writing.

Introduction

‹

"Let each person tell the truth from his/her own experience."
Florence Nightingale

When I was in Drama Club at Thompson High School, our coach, old Mr. Kevin Grasser, repeatedly emphasized the importance of beginning a story with introductions so that the theme makes sense from the very beginning. Mr. Grasser was especially emphatic about using introductions to "give context to the story." For a guy old and experienced enough to have gone to kindergarten with Shakespeare, I decided to give him the benefit of the doubt and go along with his edict. So, if we have not previously met, let me introduce myself.

My name is Catherine Wilson, but almost everyone calls me Kit. I graduated from Trail State University (TSU) in 2018 with a Bachelor of Science in Nursing. While my first year as a registered nurse (RN) was frequently difficult, and sometimes traumatic, it also provided me with soul-satisfying insights. During my second year, I started to feel more relaxed and confident at work. That said, it was still a long way before I could be considered an expert nurse. It takes a minimum of 10,000 working hours for a nurse to be considered an "expert." That's at least five years of full-time employment as a practicing registered nurse. A caveat: that timeframe doesn't factor in coping with unforeseen pestilence, which is the Biblical term for a pandemic.

I live in the Midwest of the United State. Just like the east and west coasts and southernmost states, we have some decent-sized cities where a person can find excellence in the arts, health care, education, and technology. In our cities, the full economic continuum is on display: luxury housing, by-invitation-only country clubs, and Michelin-starred restaurants located within eyesight of the poorest ghettos with shocking crime rates, few safe places for children to play, and food deserts. Our urban areas are a lot like big cities anywhere.

What sets us apart are the large sections of the Midwest that are considered rural. Farms in these areas grow three-quarters of the country's food. Cottage industry entrepreneurs often set the standards for future cultural trends. Towns and villages tend to be close-knit. Although it's a widely held belief that the only people found in Midwest rural areas are those that follow narrow-minded religious beliefs, are ultra-conservative politically, and are intolerant of diversity in any form, that is a load of baloney--and not the good baloney that you can find in the towns founded in the last 150 years by German immigrants.

It's important that I say this at the very beginning because I'm going to tell you some stories of what it's been like to be a hospital nurse during the biggest health crisis of the last 100 years. As you begin reading, you might think that you've got suburban and rural parts of the U.S. all figured out. You might think that the small towns and rural areas of the Midwest have it all wrong...or all right. But no community is completely homogeneous. There is always subtlety where humans are allowed the freedom to think and speak their minds. And that can be baffling if you're like me and just want the truth, nothing but the plain and simple truth.

I was born and raised in a small community called Thompson. It's 120 miles from TSU. I moved back "home" after graduation from nursing school. Since passing the national

NCLEX examination, I've worked as an RN in one of the adult medical-surgical units at Thompson Memorial Hospital (TMH). My community hospital is part of the more extensive TSU health care system, of which Trail State University Hospitals and Medical Center is the clinical centerpiece. Trail State is considered a progressive medical center, and its nursing and medical schools are well-known and nationally respected. My point in telling you all this is not only to dispel any notions you might have that we are dogmatic, ignorant hicks but to let you know that we struggled in 2020 with the same issues as the rest of the world.

I'd like to tell you some stories about what I experienced in the first six months of the COVID-19 pandemic.

The COVID-19 pandemic uncovered just how easily we humans can be frightened into grabbing at information even remotely logical in an effort to understand a dangerous situation. People need a certain amount of control over their lives to feel safe. We are all driven to find something or someone to believe in. Some of us were so threatened by the ambiguous nature of knowledge developed during the early months of the pandemic that we became dangerously intolerant. Confusion and fear led to a surprising number of people believing astonishingly illogical and patently false information. Some of us were so threatened that we locked ourselves away and became socially isolated and developed some goofy, even harmful thinking. Many of us, however, recognized 2020 for what it was: a situation that we had no experience with and had to painfully learn about little by little.

In 2020, the first year of the pandemic, the U.S. health care system was bombarded with higher and higher numbers of life-threatening cases from a new coronavirus. How this novel virus attacked humans was not understood. For most of 2020, only symptomatic relief could be provided to those with COVID-19 along with hopes and prayers that the body's defenses could be mobilized enough to avoid death. There was no cure or effective treatment.

For at least the first six months of 2020, those who survived depended almost exclusively on nursing care for support and treatment. But it wasn't always enough. Hundreds of thousands died. In the end, though, most of us learned to cope and developed a resilience that has made us proud in retrospect.

But back to old Mr. Grasser. He knew that as high schoolers, we could only grasp his explanation of context on a very superficial level. It takes time and life experience to make sense of information. All of us have rejected or accepted information that we had previously considered true or a diabolical plot when it was neither. Maturity broadens thinking, and careful evaluation of information reveals facts vs. fallacies. "Context" brings meaning to a situation.

I hope this introduction gives you some context to the stories in this book. If my reasoning sounds a little scattered, I am not going to blame old Mr. Grasser. Rather, I will just say my nursing colleagues and I have had a lot to do the last couple of years. Some days, we only just managed to keep our heads above the crashing waves to deliver compassionate, safe nursing care.

Thank you for reading.

Chapter One

"**Live life while you have it. Life is a splendid gift. There is nothing small about it.**"
-Florence Nightingale

The novel coronavirus was the gorilla in the room at Thompson Memorial Hospital in January 2020. No official comment came from the C-suite until February. It wasn't as though the chief executive officer, the chief financial officer, the chief nursing officer, and all the other C's were in denial. The topic wasn't exactly taboo or forbidden, but it wasn't widely discussed in public.

I went on vacation right after the new year and heard about COVID-19 from somebody on an elevator at the hotel. By the time I returned to work, the virus was mentioned in almost every Shift Report on 3 North. New information, no matter how bizarre, was shared.

Nurses are like sponges with new information—context, you know. We want to get the facts and public health perspectives. I had read various newsfeeds about the virus, which was initially called SARS COVID-19. Deaths were reported in China and some other parts of the world. At the end of January, the World Health Organization declared the virus a Public Health Emergency of International Concern. The virus was now referred to as COVID-19, after the year it was discovered.

A couple of days later, the United States issued a federal public health emergency declaration. This statement functioned as a formality to free up government public health money and limit entry into the country from areas known to be highly infectious. No one had died from COVID-19 in the U.S. ...yet.

No one I personally knew was too concerned. We were told by the federal government that this would blow over soon. It was strongly intimated that anyone who thought it was a big deal was simply foolish or purposefully trying to overexcite citizens.

I had confidence that the health care system in the U.S., however flawed, would have the resources to cope with this outbreak. One of my professors at TSU was a member of the state disaster preparedness group. At least five years ago, he told us that health care officials were proactively planning for a national medical emergency. He assured us that the U.S. had been stockpiling medical supplies and equipment in preparation for such a disaster. Teams of health care professionals were disaster-trained in nearly every state.

His presentation was both scary and reassuring. "A medical disaster is going to come. You can count on that," he told us. "It could be infectious, environmental, or from another catastrophic cause. We are anticipating and preparing so we are alert and ready."

History was on our side. We had weathered periodic SARS (Severe Acute Respiratory Syndrome) outbreaks since the first worldwide spread in 2003. SARS is caused by the same family of viruses as this new "novel" coronavirus. SARS caused ICU beds to fill rapidly and about 800 deaths were attributed to it. SARS was serious and potentially fatal, but outbreaks were seasonal, and community spread had been contained.

The hemorrhagic disease Ebola had also found its way to the United States and was quickly and effectively contained. The death rate from this hideous infectious disease worldwide is as high as 70 percent. Yet, fewer than a dozen cases occurred in the US and two people died.

There hadn't been an overwhelming worldwide medical catastrophe since the Spanish Flu pandemic 101 years before. But that was when health care officials and the general public weren't as well-informed about disease spread as we were in 2020. Nothing like that could happen in 2020 when we were so much better-informed and knowledgeable. Right?

So, in January 2020, I was aware of COVID-19 but not especially concerned. Americans were prepared. We had experience and we had supplies. We were ready.

The first official word from the hospital came at a mandatory employee meeting on Monday, February 3, 2020. Employees could choose to attend at 8 am, 4 pm, 7 pm, or midnight. Unless we had a really good approved-by-a-manager reason or were the subject of an obituary, no one could choose not to attend. The posted agenda was the novel coronavirus.

Chapter Two

"In the beginning, when this started, we knew that it
was spreading. And we knew that it also was lethal
in some percentage of people, but I don't think we
had a full appreciation about how bad it was."
-Stanley Perlman, virologist and expert on
coronaviruses University of Iowa

The morning of the mandatory meeting started out like any
other. I made my final rounds around 6 am.

Penny Grayton was my last check. She was getting ready
for discharge and a return to her assisted living home. Penny was
an 80-year-old woman with lively eyes and a Rubenesque figure, which is to say she had a generous girth. She had been on 3
North for the past three days while treated for sepsis from a uri-
nary tract infection. A UTI is not uncommon in elderly women,
especially those who aren't able to empty their bladders completely and who have difficulty with good bathroom hygiene.
Sepsis is a serious body-wide infection that can be life-threatening. In Penny's case, the bacterial cause of the infection was
identified, she received the correct IV antibiotic, and was on
her way to a full recovery. A hospital van was ready to take her
home, where she would spend another 10-12 days receiving IV
antibiotics in the rehabilitation wing of Water's Edge Assisted
Living and Rehabilitation Center.

Penny was a recent convert to the idea of staying healthy
in mind, body, and spirit. Whoever taught the wellness classes

at Water's Edge had a disciple in Penny. When I walked in, she was doing her best to convince the van transport driver to follow her health-focused path.

"Oh, Kit," she said, "I was just telling Noah here that he might want to consider a hobby to prevent mental decline. I have found reading urban fantasy novels helps keep me as sharp as I am!"

Noah, whose name badge said "Aaron" and who looked decades too young to fret about intellectual decline, glanced heavenward with a small smile and continued preparing a rolling cart and wheelchair for the 6:45 am departure. "Yes, ma'am. It's Aaron."

"Rhett, my grandson, put me onto them. Rhett, you'd think his mom was a southern belle giving a kid a name like that... Southern Comfort maybe. The woman was born and raised in Columbus, Ohio!"

She paused to laugh at her own witty daughter-in-law remark and continued. "Anyway, in this book, the Big Organization is trailing you, only you don't know it because their robotic selves look just like humans! Big O. has a seriously well-thought-out plan to destroy the world and take over our universe! Humans must find a way to identify who is a robot humanoid. Now, get this. They're afraid of kittens! That's how humans can tell if there is one of them in their presence. Their power must be deactivated before they realize the humans are onto them! Isn't that thrilling?" She sighed and closed her eyes.

"Wow," I said, wondering if the story was really that nuts-sounding or whether I was just tired after my 12-hour shift and not able to comprehend this writer's genius. If only figuring out who the good guys were came down to kittens! So much of life would be simplified.

I decided to take advantage of the quiet to hand Aaron a folder containing Penny's nursing report, her medication list, and case summary in case those who checked her in didn't get the report I'd called in yesterday evening. Aaron was the van driver and Penny's escort as well as the last step in the discharge communication hand-off.

Although I'm sure Aaron had been told this before, I wanted to remind him how hard it is to keep everyone informed when patients move from one health facility to another, such as from TMH to Water's Edge. Some patient information between health care facilities must be repeated because of the high risk of potential error. Aaron did pay attention as I gave him my spiel about the possibility of miscommunication since our two facilities don't share the same electronic medical record system. I know we repeat the same information many times, but the probability of important information getting lost or ignored was shockingly high. Aaron took the folder and promised to give it to the charge nurse when Penny arrived.

I wished her well, hoped that she would continue to recover well at home, and walked with them to the 3 North double doors. Next stop: verbal Shift Report to the day-shift nurses.

Chapter Three

"The most important practical lesson that can be given to nurses is to teach them what to observe—what symptoms indicate improvement and what the reverse."
- Florence Nightingale

Tala Denton, the other RN on my wing that night, gave me a quick wave and angled her head toward the conference room. Tala was one of my favorite colleagues. She started working at TMH about six months ago. She graduated two years before I did and was my friend Amanda Milton's roommate.

Amanda is my brother Maddy's one true love and was Tala's "Little Sis" in nursing school. It's kind of like that '90s movie *Six Degrees of Separation*. Kevin Bacon, who was a hunk in his day, said every person in the world is connected to every other person in the world by a string of no more than six friends, family, and acquaintances. That's Tala and me. She was two years more experienced than I was on paper, but eons more experienced in life.

Tala received a scholarship from the U.S. Bureau of Indian Affairs to attend college. She tells the story of how, following a disastrous tornado, she and the Sisters of the Angels and Cherubim met on her reservation. They helped her obtain a dream-come-true scholarship and whisked her off to St. Camillus College in San Davers. Tala completed her BSN in 2016 and, as a condition of her scholarship, spent three years providing nursing care with the Indian Health Service. She was the only nurse on a Navajo reservation in Arizona. Also at the clinic was one doctor who was paying back medical school loans and a receptionist/file clerk/supply manager. Working on the reservation, where nurses and physicians are at a premium, helped Tala see inadequacies in our health care system, which is why she is a staunch patient and nurse advocate. She said the work was important, and while she loved the Red Rock geography, she missed season changes and her friends in the Midwest.

I love Tala most of all because she has the best colorful language of anyone I know, and she always tells it just like she sees it. Her favorite word is "hell"—as in, "the hell you say" and "hell no!" and "all the devils in hell couldn't make me do that." Actually, "hell" is mild for her in some situations. Tala's been coached by our clinical manager to watch her language at work. She generally restrains herself...around patients and families.

I would like to be more like her, but I'm a terrible swearer and can't express my (sometimes very intelligent!) thoughts with coherence. Being an introvert has its real downsides.

Tala and I shared a wing on 3 North that night. Nursing staffing has been getting tighter. The night shift was budgeted for six nurses and one CNA (certified nursing assistant) for the entire 40-bed unit. To have an empty bed on the unit is unheard of. We have two full-time open positions on nights, so we usually work with five nurses.

When we work together, Tala and I work as a team in a 15-bed wing. We have clinical information about all the patients. We split the patient assessments, administering medications through MED (medication electronic dispenser) and documentation on TIMES (Thompson Integrated Medical Electronic System), the electronic health record. For all other things, we stay alert to help each other. Knowing a trusted colleague has my back has been one of the reasons working nights at 3 North hadn't driven me over the edge.

Since the first of the year, Tala and I volunteered as night-shift RNs for a pilot quality improvement project. It's a new approach to Shift Reports. Traditionally, Report was given in a conference room from the off-going shift to the on-coming shift. It always seemed to take longer than the allotted 30 minutes, and inevitably, a change in patient condition or a forgotten piece of information caused confusion after the last shift nurses had left.

The new approach is called Walking Report, and I thought it was working a whole lot better than some nurses had predicted. In Walking Report, we give our night nursing summary in front of each patient in their rooms. Since we have almost all private rooms, we can speak freely to the patient and each other. If a family member is in the room, we ask the patient if we can speak in front of them. If not, they are politely asked to go to the waiting room for 10 minutes. Walking Report doesn't take more than 30-35 minutes, and the patients loved it. Three things are almost always mentioned in the patient surveys: "My questions were answered when all the nurses came in," "I could show all the nurses my IV and the stuff attached to me and get it checked out," and "I could tell the nurses cared about me." It's just our wing for now, but I had high hopes for the two-month evaluation in March.

After Report, we gathered our coats, clocked out, and said goodbye to the one nurse left in the station. Meetings, mandatory or not, were not paid time for hourly employees at TMH. If we were not on the schedule to care for patients, we were not paid. Staying current with hospital information was considered part of our responsibility as TMH employees.

"Are you two going to the mandatory meeting about the COVID-19 virus?" asked Barb Mazur, the day shift charge nurse, and my former mentor.

"Hell, yes," said Tala. "I want to hear what TMH has to say about what we're doing to prepare. If it's a real thing, it'll fall on the nurses to make things work."

"Well, maybe it's going to be quickly contained," I said. "International travel into the country is cut way back, and the general message is that this is being blown way out of proportion."

"Fingers crossed that what you're saying is true," said Barb. "I hope whoever "they" are is right."

Chapter Four

"Being ready to adapt and provide essential care under crisis situations is a professional responsibility."
- Florence Nightingale

I should have known something was up when I saw the juice and coffee and bagels in the back of the conference room. TMH hospital administration never feeds staff. The hospital budget is very tightly monitored; feeding staff was considered frivolous. The only time I could remember the hospital feeding nurses was during National Nurses Week in May. Pizza and Pepsi were dropped off twice a day for the day and night staff along with a thank you gift for every nurse. Last year, the gift was a royal blue neck lanyard for our name badges that read "Thompson Memorial Loves Its Nurses." It's nice quality and I still use it. By the time I ate the pizza, it was usually cold. But it was the thought that mattered, I guess.

Harrison Phillips waved us over. Harrison is the day shift chaplain at TMH. He and I first met during one of the most confusing and scary patient experiences during my nurse residency. We've since become friends.

Harrison and I see each other regularly outside work. His Presbyterian church and my Lutheran church are neighborhood partners. This means we come together for things like Feed Your Neighbor food collections and summer Bible School for kids. Our quilting groups meet to create lap blankets for hospice patients, and our choirs give a glorious, combined concert at Christmas time.

Harrison and I are part of a group of what our churches call "young adults." It's a group of about 25 of us who are between 21 years and mid-thirties. We meet to do things like hike in the nice weather, cross-country ski in the winter, visit nearby wineries, and once, took a pottery class. Food is always part of the events, either potluck or at a restaurant with affordable prices and long tables.

Harrison and I don't date, but we get along well. He's not tall, dark, or what you'd call classically handsome, but he doesn't hurt the eyes, either. He's calm, usually upbeat, and has a wry sense of humor.

Tala and I sat down with him in the last row and began eating our bagels. I was always ravenous at the end of a 12-hour shift.

Precisely at 8 am, our CEO, Michael Weaver, took the podium. I should correct myself—Michael Weaver is Dr. Weaver, as in Ph.D. in Hospital Administration. All who worked for him were supposed to address him as Dr. Weaver. To say he thinks highly of himself and admires his own command of the business of health care would belabor the obvious.

"Good morning and thank you all for coming this morning," Dr. Weaver said.

"It's a mandatory meeting, Dr. No-Duh," muttered Tala while giving the podium an attentive smile.

"Well, first I'd like to share with you some very good news," he went on. "Our budget numbers from the end of 2019 look fantastic. Our expenses were down a bit and higher than anticipated revenue helped us recover some of the disappointment from the summer months. Good work everyone." He began to applaud, and we dutifully joined in.

Dr. Weaver nodded and grinned at the CFO sitting in the front row. His facial expression turned serious and he went on, "I also want to share with you the current information about our patient surveys. The percentage of the 'Exceed Expectations' score we all strive for is simply too low. To be perfectly honest, and you know I'm always transparent with you, it seems that sometimes patients feel as though we're rushed. Our goal is to have all our patients believe—no, we want every person who comes to us for care to know—that they are the most important person to us at that time. Our mission statement says it well: 'Every person deserves dignity and respect.' Don't you agree?"

The room was full of bobbleheads nodding agreement with the good doctor.

Michael Weaver was right on both points. We do want every patient to feel special and well cared for, and we do feel rushed more than just sometimes. There are not enough nurses to go around every shift every day. There have been some new hires recently, but it hasn't been enough to keep up with rising patient acuity and nurses leaving for other less physically demanding jobs or retiring. If even one RN calls in sick in a 24-hour period, the continuity of care for all patients can be interrupted. We have on-call 3 North nurses who come in when there is a sick call. On-call nurses are all of us RN staff who sign up for mandatory extra shifts. Speaking as a nurse who is regularly called in, I can tell you that it's no fun to work extra hours, either. Since our regular schedule is three 12-hour shifts a week (that's 36 hours), we don't get paid overtime for the extra shifts unless we work more than 80 hours during the two weeks' pay period. Another rule is that the overtime has to be approved in advance or at the request of the 3 North manager, Emily Smith.

I glanced at my watch, seeing it was almost 8:30 am. Did I misunderstand the agenda? When was the virus going to be discussed?

Dr. Weaver cleared his throat, and I saw his very flexible facial muscles change to his typical worried-concerned-empathetic expression. "Now, I want to talk with you about what is being called the novel coronavirus. I'm talking about the virus that the Chinese somehow let out of their country last year. There is a concern we may feel some effect of this, even in Thompson."

I heard a sharp intake of breath to my right, and Harrison looked aghast. "I can't believe he just said that," he muttered. "Way to go with 'every person has dignity and respect.'"

I had never heard Harrison talk like that. I was so taken aback that I almost missed the next part of Dr. Weaver's presentation.

"I know it's 8:30, but I wanted to wrap up by letting you know that TMH is prepared in case anything should come of the Chinese virus. I have directed the Nursing and Infectious Disease administrators to work with the supplies department and put together a 'coronavirus pack' for every nurses' station. It will contain an extra supply of gowns, gloves, surgical masks, shoe guards, and hand sanitizer. You who care for patients as part of our mission can feel confident we are ready. Thank you all for taking time from your day to talk together. Have a good day."

Dr. Weaver turned to leave when Tala jumped up. "Dr. Weaver? Sir? Do you have time for one quick question?"

He smiled at Tala's polite request and gestured for her to go ahead.

"Dr. Weaver, I'm Tala Denton, a night-shift RN on 3 North. Let me just say that I think you are absolutely correct. We want to give the highest quality nursing care on 3 North. I want to ask you how well things are coming along with addressing the shortage of nurses and ancillary personnel such as lab and respiratory therapy staff on the night shift. I'll sit down now and listen. Thank you."

Poor Dr. Weaver: he'd misread Tala. He'd taken her for a meek and servile young woman who only wanted the tough things explained to her by an expert.

"Yes. Well. The human resources department has a nurse recruiter who I've been assured is working tirelessly to fill all open positions at TMH. Now, 3 North has all the nurses it is budgeted for at this time. This may be an educational opportunity for you nurses to improve efficiency."

Tala stood again, but Michael Weaver continued. "It's a very complex subject and admittedly difficult to understand, but the hospital budget has many moving parts. It's not like your checking and savings accounts. Did you know that the largest expense in the budget—and its portion is massive—is caused by nursing salaries? That's right..." He shook his head in apparent shock and disbelief.

Tala said, "But isn't that because it's most of what we do here at TMH? Use nurses to deliver the highest quality care? It makes sense to me that nursing salaries should comprise the majority of the budget. Sir."

Dr. Weaver chuckled. "I know. Hospital budgets are very hard to understand. Thank you for your question and for your commitment to TMH." He turned, left the podium, and strode out a side door.

As he left, I looked up at Tala. I was a little afraid that if I breathed, I'd fan the flames of her anger.

"Well, that was bull crap," she said. "What a fuc—full pile of sh—garbage. How stupid does he think we are? I guess we just need to blame the Chinese, right? Arrogant SOB!" She sighed. "Goodbye Kit and Harrison. I think we work again together on Wednesday." She scrunched up her face and muttered, "Thanks for your commitment, my furry dog's ass...I mean tail."

She turned to leave and then turned back. "Kit, please let Emily know that I didn't use 'inappropriate language' with Dr. Big Guy and I caught my swearing in front of the preacher man." She glanced heavenward in frustration and left.

Chapter Five

"Keep good company, read good books, love good things, and cultivate soul and body as faithfully as you can."
- Louisa May Alcott

My little red Honda Civic looked especially inviting after I left Harrison and the mandatory meeting. It was going to take me home.

I had a sweet "small one-bedroom" apartment in the nicest apartment complex in Thompson. It's called the Chateau Bordeaux, and I loved the cheesiness of the name! But get this: there was underground parking and a security-coded entrance. That's not all. A fully appointed gym and so many other amazing amenities were included in the rent. I got my apartment when the building was trying to increase the number of renters and offered an almost unbelievable deal for one year. I needed to sign a two-year lease, but with the magic of automatic raises for the first five years at TMH, my salary increased enough that I could afford it even when the rent went up in November.

I got on the elevator to the third floor, joining my energetic neighbor Linda Ackerman, who was returning from her morning swim in our indoor pool.

"Hey, Kit. Good to see you. Ready for our Challah project today?" Linda asked.

"Yes! Can't wait," I said. "I don't have to work tonight so I'm going to sleep until about 1. Could I come over around 1:30?"

Linda and her husband Mark moved across the hall from me in September. They sold their big family home and downsized to the biggest apartment size available at Chateau Bordeaux. Their 3-bedroom, 3-bathroom corner unit is pretty spectacular. It has a large balcony that overlooks a park, unlike my French balcony, which is really a fancy name for a wrought iron railing outside my (one) big window overlooking the street. The Ackerman's grown children live out of town; sometimes I think they need to use their parenting skills on someone, and since I'm just across the hall, they chose me.

Linda was a baker for almost 30 years at Pixie's, the best bakery in Thompson. Although she says she's glad to have glazed her last tray of cinnamon rolls, she continues to bake at home. Sometimes the smell of yeast and spice in the hallway is enough to make me swoon. Linda shares her creations with me every week and regularly takes pies and cakes to the Salvation Army shelter near downtown.

One day, when Linda gave me a pie with fresh Michigan cherries, I'd hugged her so enthusiastically that she nearly gasped. "How about if I teach you a little baking?" she said after stepping out of my arms.

I jumped at the chance. We started with breadmaking. We have made "basic white" and "basic whole wheat" bread so far. I hadn't learned to knead or massage bread dough yet. Challah would be the first. I knew Challah bread had almost spiritual beginnings in the Jewish faith to connect with the presence of God. I also loved the visual and taste appeal of this bread.

Linda was going to show me how to punch down, knead, and eventually braid the bread dough. It would take most of the afternoon. I was pumped.

Mark was waiting at the door to their apartment. "You had a long swim today," he said to Linda. "Hi Kit, you're coming home late this morning."

"You have your observing hat on today, Mark," Linda remarked. "Kit and I were making plans for our bread-making adventure this afternoon."

"We had a mandatory meeting about the new virus," I said. "The hospital wanted us to know they're watching it. I stayed after work about 45 minutes."

"Well, they should be scared," said Mark. "I heard it was germ warfare and the Chinese are upset that we discovered it before it spread very far in the U.S."

"Where did you hear that?" asked Linda.

"At the Lodge. From a very well-connected guy whose son is a scientist. He works on highly secret projects," said Mark, lowering his voice. "The son told my guy this information is already known by the powers that be, and our people are going to stop it in its tracks. He said that something called JARS was a bad enough disease, but the new people in charge aren't going to let it get that far." He paused to stare at his wife. "I see the look on your face, Linda. If you don't believe me, then you should listen to the news. Quinn Owen's Perspective, that talk show from Channel 6 in San Davers, is going to explain everything tonight at 9:00. He's having a doctor on to expose the truth."

"I haven't heard anything like that," I said. Making a quick pivot toward my apartment door, I waved and said, "My shower and bed are calling me, so I'd better go. See you at 1:30, Linda."

As the door clicked open, I heard Mark say, "I'm glad I saw Kit. You'd think the hospital would want the doctors and nurses to know the truth."

Chapter Six

"You could be infected and have minimal symptoms, but you still have the possibility of transmitting it to someone else... Or you could be infected and have some significant lung disease that would require hospitalization and perhaps even some serious intervention...However, we do not know what this particular virus is gonna do."
- Anthony Fauci, MD, 2/26/2020

Some of the stories about this novel coronavirus were starting to sound incredibly odd, even a little crazy. Not much was known, so most of the scientific information coming out was based on what was known about other viruses in the coronavirus family. Some of the information coming from public health experts seemed confusing and contradictory. Truthfully, it was.

This murky information was maddening for Mark Ackerman, who wanted the full explanation right now. To him, anything ambiguous was just a lie or a cover-up by social media. Things have been quite polarized politically around Thompson for a few years now, and things like this virus were making it worse. I liked things as cut-and-dried as the next guy, but I also hoped someone roped me in before I mistake uncertainty for a diabolical plot.

I was also fairly sure Mark meant SARS, Severe Acute Respiratory Syndrome, not JARS. SARS had been around since I was in grade school. It was still seen in clusters from time to time and indeed caused a life-threatening illness in some people. Somewhere in the back of my mind, I remembered from an infectious disease lecture in school that SARS was a coronavirus that had jumped from bats to humans and caused around 800 deaths in this country.

"Talk about useless knowledge," I said to my walls. "Why do I remember such odd stuff? I'd rather recall every password I need for every site I used."

If there was real concern about a germ warfare attack, it would seem to me that more people would be talking about it other than the guy from the Lodge's son. Even if he did have a top-secret job.

I took off all my work clothes and put them in the laundry hamper with a lid. Then I took a shower using Christmas-scented shower gel and matching body lotion.

Feeling a whole lot better but still too anxious to sleep, I took out "Relinquished Ruminations," or "R-squared." This was the name of my journal, and I had a love-hate relationship with it. Here's a little background.

When I was just out of school, my Gram (also a nurse and one of the smartest people I knew) suggested I try writing down events and other things that frustrated me about my job. I had what I naively considered a uniquely awful time adjusting to the real nursing world after graduation, and she thought journaling might give me some clarity.

I strongly resisted admitting in writing that I felt stupid and confused. Journaling was required in my mental health and senior seminar classes in nursing school. I thought it was a huge waste of time and energy. Just the word "journal" conjured up the term "busy work." Besides, I felt foolish as a new graduate and, just in case I died, and this thing was found, I didn't want such a self-evaluation to be my legacy. However, I truly respected Gram, and I wasn't getting anywhere just wandering around alone in my brain. So, I gave up my swirling thoughts, renamed them, and started to write.

I called the journal just "Ruminations" for a while, but then went massively resonant one day and renamed it "Relinquished Ruminations." Get it? Giving up my thoughts? Surrendering my worries? Simply because I love alliteration, I titled the topic of each entry using a repeated R sound, too.

Amazingly, when I wrote what I worried about, I could think about it without so much jumbling in my brain. R-squared worked. I didn't write in it every day and sometimes not for periods of time, but when I did, I could relax and sleep better. I've been able to figure out "impossible" problems by writing. The point is that my journal taught me that my feelings sometimes live in a dangerous neighborhood in my brain, and I shouldn't wander around there alone for extended periods of time.

Chapter Seven

R-Squared: Reality-Check Ruminations

*W*e had an odd employee meeting today. I can't stop thinking about how it all ended up. Not that most of Dr. Weaver's meetings aren't always a little bit self-aggrandizing, but this was even more...odd. I can't think of another word to describe it.

The agenda was supposed to be about the new coronavirus, and Dr. Weaver talked about it for about 5 minutes. At the end of the meeting. He didn't say anything about what the hospital or our corporate system Trail State Health was thinking about it, or really anything of substance about what's being called an impending pandemic.

Pandemic...you know, a disease that spreads quickly around the world and has a high death rate? For which there is no known treatment or cure? Like nothing we've seen in this country for 100 years? And why would anyone be making it up? Why would China make vast numbers of its citizens deathly ill and put a major city on lockdown if it was a hoax? I'll tell you what, if it is a hoax then whoever thought of it and got so many people to buy into it and even die from it should be elevated to the sovereign of the world. IMHO.

Here's something even weirder: the hospital is putting together gowns and gloves and masks in a little packet for every unit. *We already have those things available, don't we? Also, are surgical masks even the right ones? We used N95 masks for SARS.*

I wonder if the chief of staff or chief nursing officer could have given more scientific information or at least a less secretive perspective about the disease caused by this virus. How different is it from SARS? You got me hanging...doesn't the administration know anything that would help nursing staff? Honestly, should nurses be left dangling if those patients might show up in Emergency? No! I say No!

Most of Dr. Weaver's presentation focused on how wonderful it was for the budget that expenses were down...isn't that because there are many openings in the department of nursing and units are working short-staffed? Revenue was up...wasn't that due to sicker patients and more patients and more insurance money coming in because they can bill for more?

Apparently, patient satisfaction surveys need to get better. We were told to do what was necessary to make patients and families believe we were not busy. Come on! I've never said to a patient, "Sorry, we're really busy and can't do everything you need today." Give me a flippin' break. It would be hard to miss that we were working quickly and nearly constantly.

We are legitimately busy, and patients are smart people who can see it. It is impossible to leisurely stroll from one patient need to another. The RNs I know organize and prioritize patient care so that when the unexpected happens, the problem can hopefully be efficiently addressed to get things back on track. I'd be sunk without my peers. Knowing that I can ask for and receive help when I need it makes the job possible.

Dr. Weaver had the brilliant idea for nurses to get some education, so we'd know how to become more efficient and look more relaxed at work. Here is me being charitable: the fact is Dr. Weaver has only the faintest idea of what bedside nursing entails. Nurses know that patients need to feel well-assessed and monitored to feel expertly cared for. There also must be enough of us to get in the rooms often enough to do these assessments and treatments. Isn't there a way to help administration and nursing understand each other better?

I've only been out of school for 19 months but trust me on this: if a nurse is observed sitting down, simply talking to a patient, discussing something with a colleague, or reading an article, then that nurse risks being called lazy or not busy enough. The nurse who is not in motion (un-busy) is considered a nurse that isn't productive enough. So, don't look too busy but don't stop moving. That should improve patient surveys. It would be a hilarious contradiction if it wasn't so awful and true.

I should invite Dr. Weaver to shadow me for a couple of nights on 3 North. It might help him learn a little bit more about working in a hospital nursing unit. I'd like to show him how we are improving efficiency with Walking Shift Report on 3 North. The patient surveys have been super good because of that.

Tala asked a good question about staffing and was blown off because the budget is too complicated for her to understand. Even Harrison wasn't his usual let-it-go self. The whole thing was odd. It felt like them versus us, and the whole atmosphere seemed very defensive. What gives?

I'm so glad to be home. Trying to be charitable has pooped me out. Later.

I put down R-squared and promptly fell asleep.

Chapter Eight

"So far, COVID-19 meets two of the three required factors to be called a pandemic: illness resulting in death and sustained person-to-person spread. Worldwide spread is the third criterion not yet met at this time."
- Nancy Messonnier MD, 2/25/2020
Director of the CDC's National Center for Immunization and Respiratory Diseases

After the first meeting about COVID-19, not much more was officially announced at TMH for about a week. We continued to see our typical 3 North winter admissions, especially those diagnosed with influenza or flu. Influenza isn't the stomach bug flu; it's a respiratory illness that can cause viral pneumonia and severe respiratory distress, especially in people over 50 and those with other chronic health conditions like chronic lung disease, diabetes, or high blood pressure. Every year, TMH sees some deaths related to influenza, but most are treatable.

In almost every case, the sickest people had not received a flu shot. Every year, it seems that the pro and con discussion about the flu shot centers on two things: that there is no guarantee that the flu shot is specific to the type of influenza spreading that year, and that you can catch the flu from the flu shot.

A person can be vaccinated and still get the flu. That is true—no argument there. But it is also true that those who have an annual flu vaccine are less likely to come into the hospital and much less likely to die if they do get the flu.

The vaccine is safe. You can't get the flu from the flu shot. Really. It's not possible. If you have aches and pains from the shot, it's probably your immune system responding as it's supposed to. It could also be from something else. But trust me, please.

Winter admissions due to cardiovascular problems were typically caused by too much exertion ("I'll just shovel those six inches of snow by using a shovel—don't need that blasted snowblower") or under exertion ("I know I'm supposed to walk and stretch for at least 30 minutes every day, but it's cold outside and *NCIS* is streaming all 500 seasons and I love Gibbs").

Bridget Place was one such patient. Bridget had moved to the United States from Ireland in the early 1950s. She met an American young man, Rob Place, who was studying at the University of Dublin and fell madly in love. Following a two-month courtship, they married and moved to San Davers. Mr. Place finished his degree at Trail State University, and then he and his bride moved to Thompson, where Mr. Place taught world history at the junior high school for a bazillion years. I never had Mr. Place as a teacher, but I knew he and Mrs. Place had nine children. Everybody in my maternal grandparents' generation went to school with at least one of the Place kids, and my parent's generation had classrooms, athletic fields, and drama/music programs packed with Mr. and Mrs. Place's grandchildren. Mr. Place passed away a few years ago.

Bridget Place was an energetic woman who lived alone without problems until hypertension, diabetes, and poorly controlled angina placed her on 3 North. Three days prior, while trying to steam-clean her own carpets, she felt faint and had dull chest pain. She made her way to the coffee table where her EMS necklace lay. Pressing the button, she was able to call 911. She did not experience a myocardial infarction (MI) or heart attack. Her unstable angina was the cause of inadequate blood flow to her heart during this period of overexertion.

Mrs. Place rang for the nurse at 3:45 am. I knew from Report that this was the time she usually woke at home. My guess is that with all those kids, she had no time for herself unless she got up extremely early.

"Kit, you are just wonderful to worry about me," said Bridget Place. "I didn't survive raising nine hellions whom I adored and babysitting 23 grandchildren to not be in good health. I'm ready to go home, so let's talk about what's what. Then you tell the daytime people to tell the doctor that I am ready to go. Are you with me, darlin'?"

I could listen to Mrs. Place talk all day. She preferred to be called "Mrs." because "it's more polite and we aren't close friends, are we, pet?" Her Irish lilt was strong and musical, and her face was flawlessly wrinkled. Coupled with a request to talk to me about caring for herself at home, I was hooked.

"Of course, Mrs. Place," I said. I pulled up her discharge plan on the TIMES medical record and we started talking.

We reviewed her medications, diet, and activity recommendations. A blood pressure monitoring service was available that would transmit a daily reading to her cardiologist. She correctly demonstrated applying and using the cuff. She said she understood that even though she could save money by steam-cleaning her own carpets, it was probably a good idea to request help from one of her able grandchildren. That caveat also applied to washing windows, hanging drapes, and shoveling snow. We talked about keeping an adequate supply of all her medications, especially nitroglycerin under her tongue when she felt acute angina pain. I agreed to tell the day shift about her readiness for discharge during Walking Report.

"It's up to you, Mrs. Place," I said. "But you may want to seriously think about wearing the medical alert necklace that can call 911. Pardon me for saying so, but it was the luck of the Irish that the device was so close when you got sick."

"You're right," she laughed. "I've been lucky, but 88 years is old enough to stop doing everything with no help. I don't want to break a hip and have to go into a home." She paused and took a deep breath. "I'd like to live through this virus, too, you know. I saw some awful diseases at home before moving to America. Pneumonia killed my sister and brother in 2005. And they were just 70 and 72 years old."

"Oh dear," I quietly said, and Mrs. Place nodded.

"Now you get out of here. I need to rest before you nurses come barging in at 7:00."

Certain patients stick in my mind because of the time they entered my life. I remember Mrs. Place because she was discharged on Wednesday, February 26, 2020, the day the first two acknowledged U.S. deaths from COVID-19 were reported in Washington state. I knew Mrs. Place was at high risk for complications and death if she contracted COVID-19. I also knew her family would have their hands full trying to keep her home in quarantine.

Chapter Nine

"Amid a coronavirus outbreak in the United States, the U.S. Centers for Disease Control and Prevention is encouraging older people and people with severe chronic medical conditions to stay at home as much as possible."
- Elizabeth Cohen, Senior Medical Correspondent, 3/6/2020 CNN HEALTH

In March, the TMH nursing department began to prepare in earnest for possible COVID-19 cases. Our chief nursing officer, Stephanie Porter, DNS, RN was alert to the experiences in larger cities. She had been in close communication with the largest hospital in our system, Trail State University Hospital (TSUH) in San Davers.

Our hospital is designated by the state as a community hospital. We don't have large intensive care units or the number of advanced trained staff that TSUH does. What Stephanie ("please don't call me Dr. Porter when we are working together as a professional nursing team") did tell us about this virus was sobering.

Through twice-weekly communications in early March, she shared with us that although the threat of COVID-19 coming to Thompson was still considered low, there were cases reported in San Davers and the surrounding communities. These cases increased every day, and the patient outcomes were grim. All patients who had been placed on ventilators had died. Not all patients needed ventilators but predicting the disease progression was not yet possible.

There was no medical treatment known to be effective. Care was supportive and almost exclusively nursing-centered.

Stephanie designated 3 North as the ICU overflow unit for COVID-19 cases if that need arose. Our manager Emily Smith coordinated the three-pronged attack: personal protective equipment/PPE, unit redesign, and construction.

Other hospital departments requested in-services to update their staff on these precautions. Harrison asked if I could talk to the chaplaincy department, and Emily agreed. Here is how it went and what I told them:

Now, picture this information delivered with attractive and informative PowerPoint slides in a huge conference room where the six TMH chaplains, two Roman Catholic priests, and the Muslim Imam on-call for the hospital were seated around the room wearing masks and sitting at least six feet apart. It was the first time I'd ever been a speaker for a whole department. I was more than a little apprehensive, but spoiler alert: it went fantastically well. So, in a not-at-all humble way, I still share this feat with anyone who will listen.

> • *COVID-19 is a very real threat that is causing death and disease around the world. It is the worldwide spread that makes this outbreak a pandemic. It's a new virus to humans. It is spread through the air.*
>
> • *Personal Protective Equipment, or PPE, means gloves, masks, face shields, and gowns that cover the arms. They are to be used by everyone entering a room where the patient has COVID-19. We know from conversations with the nursing administration in San Davers and at TMH that there aren't enough gowns or gloves to provide the best possible protection for nurses. To prepare for this, sets of three hooks have been attached to the patient side of every door. Gowns are to be hung up on the hooks after use and reused until wet or soiled.*

• *All the ICU and 3 North nursing staff are annually fitted for N95 masks. This year, nurses were fitted with their own N95 masks. Masks are to be used with any patient contact until further notice and reused until it rips or is soiled.*
• *If the nurses aren't at work, their N95 masks are to be stored in paper lunch bags with the nurse's name on them. Paper bags are breathable and can clean a mask in about 24 hours. A new paper bag is used each time the mask is stored because it gets dirty from cleaning. In 3 North, we have designated a windowsill for these bags.*
• *If you have a choice of a cloth mask or an N95, use the N95. This is why: the N95 mask can filter very small particles, up to 0.3 microns. That is really, really small. There are 25,000 microns in an inch. The COVID-19 virus is even smaller. But because the virus always hooks a ride with something bigger, it can be stopped by an N95 mask.*
• *You might have heard through the grapevine or from some news outlets that N95 masks don't work because they can't filter particles as small as COVID-19. Not true. Viruses are tricky free-loaders. Viruses are literally parasites. Viruses will die unless they are attached to something alive like mucous or water in the air you breathe from your nose and mouth. That means that the inhaled COVID-19 virus is bigger than the N95 filtration size because it's attached to something bigger. N95 masks are effective against COVID-19.*

- *As a chaplain, you will be asked to wear a mask in the hospital, especially if you're near a patient who needs your spiritual support. At this time, I don't have information about the chaplain mask protocol. Now that you know about N95 masks, you can contribute your knowledge to the discussion.*

- *Beginning March 1st, all 3 North rooms were made private. A number of portable nurses' desks were placed in the halls to allow nurses to computers for TIMES charting, physician orders, and test results. A linen closet in the hall has been converted to hold the medication electronic dispensers (MEDS). The door to this closet is locked and can only be opened by nurses and pharmacists who have been given name badge access.*

- *The Central Nurses Station in 3 North is gone. Only the cardiac monitor technicians and the unit clerks remain in the center of the unit where the wings split off. We call it Central Station; all communication from that area now comes to nurses' pagers or on TIMES. No one else is allowed in Central Station.*

- *Four telephones have been placed in each hallway so that nurses and other clinicians can call or answer without going into the Central Station.*

- *Hand sanitizer and wipes are placed near these telephones and in every room. Use them often.*

- *Finally, special ventilation alterations are nearly finished. These are negative airflow rooms. In hospitals, special ventilation is either positive airflow or negative airflow.*

- *The cleanest rooms in the hospital are positive airflow. Places like operating rooms and rooms for patients with poor immune systems have positive airflow. The air inside the room can circulate out to the hallway but is not allowed back in the room. Positive airflow protects the people in the room.*

- *In cases of respiratory infectious disease, negative airflow is best. The air in these rooms can come in through the hall but is not allowed to go out of the room back to the hallway. The air is vented outside, which protects people who are not in the room. Seven rooms on 3 North have been temporarily converted to negative airflow.*

- *Here's a fun fact: did you know the bathroom in your house is negative airflow? If you turn on the bathroom fan, any odors are blown outside and not back into your house.*

I finished this presentation in 30 minutes and was so relieved when it was over. The chaplains asked a couple of questions and even clapped at the end! Harrison was thrilled. He hugged me and gave me a forehead kiss, and I realized I was starting to like him more like a man, not just a friend. Know what I mean?

Chapter Ten

R-Squared: Responsibility Ruminations

*C*OVID-19 has me on hyper-alert waiting for...something. I feel like Chicken Little. The sky is falling! The sky is falling!

COVID-19 is in San Davers and my college suitemates Erin and Mary say it has been beyond awful. They say working in full PPE with patients who go into multiple organ failure and die in the blink of an eye is frightening and exhausting. One patient was a staff nurse on their unit. She died within four days of being exposed at a wedding reception. Erin and Mary said it was like a horror movie.

The hospital is trying to do what is right. We're as ready as we will ever be just in case COVID-19 comes to Thompson. At first, I worried that the construction and redesign of 3 North would bother our patients, but that's not a concern at all. However, there's been a huge change in the TMH census.

Elective surgeries have been canceled, and the hospital census has plummeted. I've been floated to 3 South during this time because 3 North is closed. People still become ill and emergency admissions are continuing. Because the night shift has one full-time open RN position on both 3 North and 3 South, I've only been told to stay home one night without pay because there were "too many nurses."

Tala was beside herself. "I still don't get why it is perfectly fine for us to work short-staffed when call-ins or open positions exist, but it is not OK to have one extra nurse when there are adequate numbers of staff. The nurse is in the budget anyway."

Once Tala gets going, there is no stopping her. "Let's not friggin' forget, Dr. Weaver thinks understanding the hospital budget is beyond a nurse's brain capacity."

The smart thing to do at this point is to acknowledge Tala's frustration. If she doesn't get a response, she continues, "Hell, I think—no, I know! —he acts like he thinks nurses are working on an assembly line like we're making cars with predictable steps, no surprises, and certain outcomes. You don't have to draw me a stinkin' picture. No patients, no nurses. How about sending some of the C-suite suits home? If there aren't nurses doing the work that management people think they supervise and analyze, then what do they have to do? Give them a few weeks off without pay."

It's hard to disagree too strongly with Tala's logic. Aside from objecting to her language if she spouts off where patients and families can hear, I haven't heard even one nurse object to her principles.

Sip and Stitch, my face-to-face support group, is on hold because everything is closing down. We still have our chat room though and that is keeping me sane. We share what we've read or have heard, and bounce information off each other. We try to bolster each other through positive affirmations and humor.

Tala's continued problem with her colorful language was the topic this week. She let loose using the B-word to describe a patient whose behavior she found distasteful, then used the F word as an adjective for the assertion. Someone from the lab heard her. This time, she got a written warning. This was formally strike one for her.

To be fair, Tala has gotten out of control with these expletives. It's hard to believe she feels the dignity of every person under our care (from TMH mission!) when she talks like that.

I do love her, but this has to stop. She could be fired, and then where would I be?

At the end of the day, it's still all about me!

Sip and Stitch loved this. Everyone chimed in with different, less vulgar terms for her to use. Here are a few:

Barb: What the frog?

Susan: Crap

Patrick: Crapola

Rosie: Eat sheep

Diane: Bull spit

Jacob: Sorry to be so late to this party. I want to speak out on behalf of the F word. It is extremely useful. It describes a multitude of attitudes and feelings.

Tala: The mask is going to block a lot of words. I'm not worried.

Me: You know, Tala should be commended for not really cursing. She doesn't take the Lord's name in vain.

Barb: Really? Is that the best you've got, Kit? As long as we avoid deity names, we can feel comfortable letting loose, is that what you mean? Jacob, have you lost your mind? And Tala, hells bells, I'd be shocked if you were worried.

Susan: Oh, Kit, for the love of Pete!

Patrick: Aren't you dating the chaplain, Kit? Ask him what he thinks about your narrow definition of swearing!

Me: We're not dating, just really good friends, and I said cursing, not swearing. Tala, please stop swearing. I don't want you to get fired...and yes, this is mostly about how your swearing firing would affect me.

Rosie: I suppose you're technically right, Kit, but really. Potato Patato. Crass is crass.

Diane: I don't give a Donald Duck! I agree with Jacob. I also find the F word to be versatile. But. Not. At. Work.

Me: How about bar of turd? I think I can sleep now. Thank you, my good friends.

Chapter Eleven

R-Squared: Repetitive Ruminations

*I*can't stop thinking about work stuff. It's 2:00 in the afternoon. *I'm supposed to be asleep. I have to work tonight after Sunday supper at Mom and Dad's. I wrote and ruminated this morning. That's supposed to help me relax, so why can't I sleep now?*

The low hospital census is totally terrifying me because the grapevine says Dr. Weaver is having fits and slashing parts of the budget. No elective surgeries can be scheduled, and hospital outpatient services are closed. This means a whole lot less money coming in. Hospital staff from those services are being furloughed.

According to the hospital communications, I should be reassured that staff is being furloughed instead of laid off. Furlough is different from being laid off because furloughed staff still receive benefits like health care. Furloughed staff are still considered employees, and they are supposed to be off for "only" a designated period of time. You can be paid if you're furloughed, but you have to use our accumulated time off or ATO, which is what most of the world calls vacation time. Sick time can't be used; sick time is like insurance given to employees because of the hospital's goodwill. It's not considered ATO. Ha! I have 24 hours of ATO: that's two days in my world.

On the other hand, if a nurse is laid off, they can get unemployment checks but no health benefits. And then, when staff is called back to work, they must reapply for their jobs. That's because to be laid off really means you were fired. The hospital says they promise to hire anybody back who gets unemployment. No worries, right? What great news. In the middle of a pandemic, I'd lose my health benefits.

The administration won't say in advance to whom or when furloughs will happen. Human resources have told the furloughed outpatient nurses that they hope it will only be for "about three weeks or so." I'm darn sure that going three weeks—minus two days—without a check is not going to work for me.

I have savings. I'd rather work than use savings. None of the administrators or managers are taking pay cuts. Why not furlough the same percentage of administrators and managers? Tala is right. Nurses are expendable. Hell.

More scary stuff: nobody knows enough about COVID-19, so the rules keep changing. Giving discharge advice to patients is not clear-cut as any of us would like. Lots of people want black-and-white answers. Mask or no mask? Wash groceries or not necessary? Open schools and stores and churches or not? Try this medicine or too dangerous? Whenever some new information surfaces and the rules change, the more frightened a lot of people become. The more things change, the more I hear people say they're being lied to by powerful people who want to ruin their lives. That's causing huge problems keeping safe with masks and gloves and handwashing. We will never get rid of COVID-19...or even get it under control...if it keeps on like this.

Do you know what I think? COVID-19 is all we hear about. It's too much information. I think that when the brain is bombarded with complicated and differing information, it gets overwhelmed. Then what is left of the smart parts of the brain just makes up or accepts explanations that sort of make sense.

That happened to me a lot when I was first out of nursing school. I kept thinking that people were purposefully trying to fool me and make me look stupid. I was able to feel stupid without any help. It seemed like I was so stressed, that I couldn't make the simplest connections. Like this: I learned in school that "every person is an individual." Then after graduation, I was told that people experience some similar and different ways of coping with the same disease state. So, which is it? Is everyone the same or is everyone different? How can you tell? Hard to believe, but that made sense to my swamped brain. Things changed too much and too fast when I was first out of school, and my brain reverted to "you are not telling the truth" or "that's not how I learned it, so you are stupid." It took me almost two months to remember the C word: context.

I get it. If you know the right buttons to push, it's easy to fool frightened people. We all want to have safety in our personal worlds. COVID-19 is massively unsafe. I keep hearing about people who have no clue, but confidently say things that are wrong. Like anybody should be able to see that some explanations are totally wrong. But no. The goal seems to be to find people who are confident and give definite answers. Those answers are likely to be trusted. If a doctor or scientist or nurse says that COVID-19 knowledge isn't complete yet, they risk being called stupid or a liar. It feels like a no-win situation.

Do you know what else I hear at work that shocks me? If a person also makes fun of people who have a different view, that makes other people feel better. Is that weird or what? It's like "Aha! I can't be tricked by you. You can't make me feel dumb! You're dumb...no, you're dumb...no you're ugly...no, you're double ugly." It's turning us into little kids. Bratty little kids.

Calling things murky today on March 15th, 2020, is probably generous. I wear a mask all the time at work except for eating and sit as far away as I can from other people at work.

The truth is that there is not always enough room to make the distance six feet. Is six feet enough? Jeez Louise.

Fear is powerful. Dear God, help me listen to as many sides to this as I can without shutting down my brain. Keep me from the temptation to make fun of or hate people who don't think like me. Amen.

That's it for now. I've finished my sermon to self. Feeling a little better. One more hour until the alarm. Later.

Chapter Twelve

"Toilet paper became a coveted item in late March
when many cities and states across the country issued
shelter-in-place orders in response to the coronavirus
pandemic. Many attribute the shortage to disruptions in
the supply chain. But the supply chain remains strong.
The shortage is actually the result of panic buying."
-Dr. Ronald Gonzalez, Assistant Professor Conversion
Economics and Stability, North Carolina State University.

Mom had dueling themes for Sunday dinner on March 15th:
St. Patrick's Day and COVID-19. I had no idea what she
was going to do for the COVID-19 part of dinner, but I couldn't
wait for corned beef and cabbage, potatoes, carrots, and—my
contribution! —Irish Soda Bread.

Linda, my neighbor, and bread-making coach walked me
through the Irish Soda Bread recipe. We made three loaves. One
for us to taste-test, one for Sunday dinner, and one for the home-
less shelter. The taste test was a success. The texture was light,
and it had just enough raisins. Sour cream turned out to be this
bread's secret! I felt so grateful to Linda for taking me under her
baker's wing.

I was scheduled to work that night, so I asked my mom if
we could eat at 5 pm so I could get changed and leave for work
by 6:20 pm. When I arrived at my childhood home at 4:30, the
conversation coming from the kitchen was loud. There was no
laughing. Loud voices and no laughing can only mean one of

two things: my dad didn't put in his Miracle-Ears or there was a bone of contention between my siblings and/or parents. This time, it was the latter.

Maddy, my younger brother, had been laid off from his job at the lumber yard last Wednesday. He was working there full-time while also attending the community college, majoring in construction. Because of COVID-19, his college was closing for a week before beginning online classes.

Maddy was standing near the kitchen island with his arm around his girlfriend and my nurse friend, Amanda Milton. Since everyone in our family has a nickname and our family loves Amanda, we call her Mandy. Mandy and Maddy had been dating hot and heavy for about 18 months. If Maddy had his way, they would be living together, but Mandy is holding out until Maddy finishes school and gets a real job.

Mandy had a tough time right out of school. She completed the nurse residency in the outpatient clinics at TMH because she absolutely hated bedside nursing. It turned out that she enjoyed clinics better than hospital unit nursing. But nursing is full of career opportunities, and Mandy kept her eyes open. A nurse from a pharmaceutical company had visited her clinic to explain a new drug. He and Mandy talked after the in-service, and he told his boss about her. The boss contacted Mandy and asked her to interview for a new position. Mandy was offered an honest-to-goodness superb nursing job as a nurse in the research division of the drug company. She worked with volunteers in clinical trials for new drugs. She also thrived on working with data and spreadsheets to understand the cellular effects of medications on people. She made about one-and-a-half times as much as I did, and she had a company car, mileage allowance, and per diem expenses for meals and hotels if she has to be out of town. The salary and perks were astonishingly good compared to a hospital bedside nurse. Although I was a little jealous of her disposable income, that job would bore me to tears. On day one,

I'd be found asleep on my keyboard with data analysis running across the screen.

Maddy was loudly and confidently expounding on the idea that COVID-19 was a hoax, perpetrated to ruin the economy. In addition, he was mighty upset that masks, social distancing, and handwashing were being forced on him.

Dad was trying to explain that COVID-19 was real and dangerous, and no one was trying to force him to do anything that wasn't needed for his safety. My dad went on to say that social distancing was designed to protect him and other people.

Mandy was nodding her head vigorously. "Maddy, honey, it's a real thing and it could get really bad."

I put down the soda bread and said, "Maddy, if you think this isn't a real thing, you are kidding yourself. It's dangerous and is called a pandemic, you know, worldwide. It's a national emergency in this country, bro. Tomorrow, the state is closing down schools and businesses not to make your life miserable but to try to stop the spread. If there is no one to spread it, the virus will die out. That's how viruses work."

Mom started dishing up dinner and handed the corned beef to my big brother Teddy to cut. Teddy and Mom were teachers.

"I'm not sure that I can teach third graders in a virtual class-room," Mom said with a little quiver in her voice.

"It's going to take some getting used to," said Teddy. Teddy taught math at the high school.

It was probably a roll of the dice who had the most chal-lenging situation: Mom with nine-year-olds who weren't used to learning anything online except the newest game, or high school students who didn't see the point of sitting through school in person or online. Kids of all ages were incredibly technically sophisticated and could play games while appearing to be engaged in an online classroom.

It turned out Mom and Teddy were right to be leery. That's a story for another day, though.

"Hello, family! Does anybody care about my feelings?" asked my baby brother Kai, who was a senior in high school this year. "What's going to happen to the Class of 2020? What about prom? What about the junior-senior basketball game? What about the senior trip to New York City to see Broadway plays? It's a bunch of crap. We're being cheated!"

"Watch your language, Kyle, my son," said Dad, using Kai's given name. "This is nothing anyone alive has experienced before. It's been 100 years since the last pandemic. This is a new virus and a new situation. I promise you that we will celebrate the class of 2020. I'm not confident about Broadway and the prom. A lot of it will depend on whether we can run the virus into the ground with social distancing and masks and hand hygiene."

"Okay, Andrew, Catherine, Matthew, Amanda, Edward, and Kyle," Mom announced, using everyone's full first names. "Let's sit down and eat."

After saying the table grace from our childhood, we started eating and the temperature cooled in the room. My soda bread was a huge hit, and the boiled dinner was delicious.

Dad and the boys cleared the dishes. Dad stayed in the kitchen, and I heard giggling.

Mom motioned to Teddy, who stood up and made the sound of a trumpet. "And here's Mom and Dad!"

Mom and Dad formally marched out together. Mom was carrying a lemon meringue pie and Dad was carrying a wrapped gift for everyone. They momentarily stunned us into silence.

"Here are your gifts." We looked at each other and unwrapped...a roll of toilet paper!

"Look at the pie. Do you see the spikes in the meringue? Like the COVID-19 virus? The pie is a sign that some sour times are coming up."

That did it. The tension broke, and we all laughed.

"Good one, Dad!"

"COVID-19 meringue peaks? Mom, I love it."

I looked at my watch and saw that it was 5:45. Enough time to eat pie and get ready to leave for work.

"Somebody's phone is ringing in the kitchen," said Mom. Because of Mom's no-phone-or-other-electronic-devices-at-the-dinner-table rule, everyone except the parents stood up and headed for the kitchen.

"It's Kit's," my siblings groaned.

I answered an unfamiliar number. "Yes, this is Catherine Wilson."

When I got back to the table, everyone stopped talking and looked at me. I wondered if I looked as flushed as I felt.

"I've been furloughed," I said.

Chapter Thirteen

"Hospital inpatient days dropped in the first quarter
of 2020...a decrease of 10.8%...due to fewer elective
surgeries being scheduled during the early part
of the pandemic as recommended by the Centers
for Medicare & Medicaid Services (CMS)."
- United States Census Bureau

I punched down the raised bread dough, then I slapped it on the counter that had been dusted with flour and kneaded it just as Linda taught me. Well, I may have pushed and pulled it a little too much before slamming it back into the bowl for the yeast to proof into another raised ball.

The bread would either be heavy as a stone or light and airy. I could never remember what happened if I kneaded dough too much. I'd have to text Linda and ask her because I couldn't go over to her apartment. She was not in my "safe bubble" of people during quarantine. My family was not in my safe bubble, either. I couldn't even see them after today until quarantine lifted.

What was I going to do? I was furloughed. After my two vacation days were used, I had no money coming in for...who knows how long. I had rent to pay. Cable and electricity bills. Food and gas to buy. Sirius XM, too, for crying out loud! What was I going to do?

Since I wasn't at work, I was supposed to stay away from people at work. But since I'd just been at work last week, I couldn't see anybody I hadn't worked with, either. For at least 14 days, that is, and that was if I didn't get COVID-19.

My FaceTime ring sounded. It was Harrison. We decided that we would be in each other's safe bubble. He knew I was worried and asked if he could come over tonight with a pizza.

He looked tired, although I only saw his eyes and eyebrows over his N95 mask. He really needs to trim those eyebrows, I thought.

"Where are you going to get a pizza?" I asked. "All the restaurants are closed."

"I have discovered store-bought frozen pizza," he said. "An amazing product."

"Okay, you got me," I said. "I've got salad here and I'm baking some honey wheat bread. That's a lot of bread along with pizza, but you can take some home."

"I get off at 4:30," he said. "I'll swing by home, shower, and change into non-hospital tainted clothes. How about if the pizza and I are there at 6?"

At 6:01 pm, my lobby doorbell rang. It was Harrison and I buzzed him in.

I had to smile when I noticed his attire. He had showered and smelled like Dial soap. He wore a black and white Henley shirt with blue jeans. He looked like a walking bruise.

Nevertheless, we hugged enthusiastically. It was good to see another person who was not on TV, in full PPE, or in a hospital bed.

Taking the frozen carton from his hands, I walked into the kitchen. Actually, in my very wonderful but not spacious apartment, the hallway led directly into the kitchen, which was also the same room as my living room and my dining room. Efficient.

In two steps, Harrison sat on the sofa and sighed.

"Let me get this in the oven, get you a soda, and we'll talk," I said.

"That's a great plan," he said.

Harrison said he had a tough time describing the atmosphere at the hospital. It was like waiting for a punch that you hope wouldn't come, but you sort of wish would come so you could get it over with. There was the unspoken worry about more nursing furloughs; physical therapy, occupational therapy, the labs, and radiology departments also had staff furloughed. The census remained low.

Neither of us was sleeping well. I know I had circles under my eyes, and Harrison looked drained, too.

"It's funny, you know, Kit?" he said. "I'm grateful that we don't have COVID-19 in Thompson, and I think that keeping people out of circulation is a good idea until the country can get out a better supply of PPE. I keep thinking that if the state health department is right, we can drive COVID-19 away in about three weeks. But that means that everybody stays away from others. That's not happening."

"I know," I said. "You know my neighbors across the hall, the Ackerman's?"

"Linda, your baking teacher?"

"Yep. Well, her husband is Mark and he's convinced the scientists are wrong and there is no reason for quarantine. He belongs to some fraternal lodge downtown. They're a private club and he says they don't have to follow state guidelines. He goes to his lodge every day and hangs around with who knows how many other Einsteins and comes home to his wife. Linda is worried and she even let slip that one of the lodge guys was hospitalized with COVID-19 while visiting his adult son and wife, grandkids, and sister who live in San Davers."

"Really? That could be considered a first Thompson case," said Harrison.

"Scary, right? Linda and I don't see each other anymore, although we talk by text every day."

"How's the lodge guy doing?"

"Well, Linda has said that he was only in the hospital for five days and didn't need a ventilator. So, they sent him home to his sister's house to recover. Mark says he's just fine; no problem at all, just a false alarm," I said. "Linda didn't say if the son, wife, kids, and sister got sick, and Mark was pretty defensive. He just said the guy will be back in Thompson this weekend."

"Help us all," Harrison prayed out loud.

The pizza wasn't too bad, and we tried to find other less emotional topics to talk about. We taste-tested my bread, which wasn't too bad considering that I had practically kneaded it into submission after the first rise.

"Well, Kit, let me ask about the elephant in the room," Harrison said with a side glance. "How's furlough going?"

I didn't realize how close to the surface my fear was. My eyes teared and I gasped a little. "It's terrible. I have no money coming in. I could apply for unemployment, but I haven't done that. I'm not going to ask my parents for money—they've got Maddy living there with no job. I could dip into savings, but I just want to work. I'm scared."

Harrison put his arms around me and let me cry. He patted my hair and kissed my cheeks. "It's OK, my dear friend," he said. "I actually have an idea that might be way out. Now, it might be a lame-brained idea, but maybe not."

I hiccupped. "Go on. I'll listen to just about anything."

"The chaplaincy department at Trail State University Hospital is overrun with very sick COVID-19 patients. Many of these patients are passing away with no family present since there is a no visitation policy in all the hospitals." He paused. "The executive director of supportive services is our administrative boss. He's asked for chaplain volunteers to come to San Davers to help. Eric Cone, the afternoon chaplain, volunteered and he starts there tomorrow."

That little tidbit caused me to feel a twinge of hope. "Do you think they need nurses?" I asked. "I would do anything. My Gram and my suitemates Erin and Mary live there. I'd have a place to stay."

Harrison pulled me closer. "I have no idea about their nursing needs, but it's worth a call to human resources to volunteer."

"Oh my gosh, Harrison," I said sitting up. "I could kiss you!"

And I did. Holy Toledo, did I ever! It was like electricity coursing through me. What the…?

I think Harrison must have felt something, too, because when we pulled apart, he stood up and said, "Well, that was unexpected. Nice. Unexpected. I'd better go. Yes. Nice. Thanks for the stuff, pizza and bread, and stuff. I'll talk to you soon, probably tomorrow, maybe."

We hugged again, grinned at each other, and he left.

I skipped to my bedroom, one and a half skips because it was so close to the living room. My computer booted right up, and I started an email to Colleen McKurk, the nurse recruiter at TMH.

> **Hello Colleen,**
> **My name is Catherine Wilson. I'm an RN on 3 North at TMH and have been furloughed due to low census. I'd like to talk with you about ways my skills as a medical-surgical unit RN could possibly be used in another capacity during this time. May I call you tomorrow? Thank you for considering this request.**

I finished the dishes and checked my email before turning off the computer.

There was an answer. No way! It was 8:15 pm!

> **Hi Catherine,**
> **Thank you for contacting me about your willingness to work in other areas of need as an RN in our Trail State University**

Health System during your furlough. I would be very interested in hearing your ideas and letting you know what opportunities might be available.

Please call me tomorrow. My number is 555-937-0001. I will be available at 10:00 am, if that is convenient.

Sincerely,
Colleen McKurk, BSN, RN
Nurse Recruiter

And that's how I started to work during my furlough at Trail State University Hospital in San Davers.

Chapter Fourteen

R-Squared: Relieved Ruminations

*I*can't believe how well the call went with human resources. *They are looking for RN help at TSU Hospital. They're organizing a small group of nurses, respiratory therapists, and physical therapists who would be exclusively involved in proning patients in the intensive care and ICU-step down units caring for COVID-19 patients.*

Proning means placing a patient on their belly or "prone position" instead of on their backs, which is called "supine position." It helps people who are in severe respiratory distress because it gives the lungs more room to expand.

Because it takes at least five people to turn a critically ill patient to the prone position, a prone team is being formed. This is to free up intensive care unit RN time for other nursing needs of very ill COVID-19 patients. I'm going to be a prone team member and live in San Davers.

Gram lives in San Davers. She is still working, but in a smaller hospital, and not with COVID-19 patients. Gram is over 60 years old, so is high-risk. It wouldn't be safe to stay with her if I'm going to work with COVID-19 patients all day.

So, I'm going to live with Mary and Erin. They both work with COVID-19 patients at the university hospital and their safe bubble sounds like fun and professional people. They are thrilled to have me coming and have cleared a space in their living area for my air mattress. I hope we still get along as well as we did as suitemates in nursing school! I'm excited to be finally able to get in the middle of this crisis.

Chapter Fifteen

March 17, 2020 "West Virginia reports its first COVID-19 case, meaning the disease is present in all 50 states."
Eric Schumaker ABC News

My first day at Trail State University Hospital (TSUH) was Friday, only three days from the evening I'd contacted Colleen, the nurse recruiter. She was a role model of efficiency. I was pumped.

Email instructions were brief and specific:

1.	Bring your own scrubs. They must be the blue RN color required at all hospitals in the Trail State System. You will launder your own scrubs.
2.	Don't bring any PPE or medical equipment that was not issued from TSUH.
3.	Meet in Mezzanine Conference Room G at 6:45 am. Refer to the attached map for parking and entrance instructions.
4.	Coffee and a continental breakfast will be provided.
5.	Cafeteria services are not available. Plan accordingly.
6.	Orientation to the Prone Team will begin at 7:00 am. Plan to stay a full 12-hour shift.
7.	Further scheduling will be communicated at orientation.

That was as much as I knew.

I packed my backpack and air mattress on Thursday afternoon. My little red Honda Civic made it to San Davers in just under two hours. Nothing, other than one gas station, was open on the way down, so no latte for me. I arrived around 5 pm, and as promised, drove first to Gram's house, parked in her driveway, and beeped.

Gram was my best nursing resource and confidant. She had over 40 years of continuous experience specializing in cardiac nursing. Right now, she was back in scrubs and working 8-hour shifts in the coronary care unit (CCU) at TSU St. Luke's Hospital. This has helped release the critical care nurses to care for COVID-19 patients in the ICUs. We talked last night, and she told me about what TSU nurses are doing to cope with the flood of patients admitted to the hospital with COVID-19.

The CCU wasn't supposed to admit any patients with COVID-19, but there was literally no way to guarantee a person didn't have COVID-19. So, in Gram's unit, every patient was presumed to be contagious. There hadn't been enough COVID-19 tests, so only people with symptoms have been tested. I know public health statistics need to be kept about the number of people who have positive COVID tests. But using COVID-19 tests which are in short supply to check people who almost undoubtedly have COVID seems like trying to fix a problem with the damage already done. Do you know the expression about closing the barn door after the horse has run away? Well, that's how Gram made it sound.

She wore an N95 mask and gloves when caring for all her patients. COVID-19 is so contagious, and its spread is so subtle, that even patients who look fine may be highly contagious. It could take up to two weeks from the time of exposure until symptoms develop. During that time, a person could spread the virus and not know. But that wasn't what I thought was the scariest of all: some people who have COVID-19 and are highly contagious never show any symptoms. So, like Typhoid Mary, infectious people could spread COVID-19 without seeming sick at all.

Gram was 64 years old, and although she was healthy and energetic, her age was getting up there. She was considered at high risk for serious complications and death if she became infected with COVID-19.

Gram knows this stuff, but she's a nurse and didn't flinch when she was asked to care for patients. She stayed well-informed and wasn't fooling herself about this respiratory infection. She didn't have direct social contact with anyone outside of work. When she came home from work, the scrubs came off and she showered.

Today, she was out of scrubs and wearing yoga pants and a long shirt. She had a headband on and no makeup—just out of the shower. She waved at me from the porch, threw me a kiss, and motioned "good luck." I motioned that we would stay in touch by text and phone calls. We both sent a thumbs-up and I pulled back out to the street. My Gram understood me. So far, so good with no close social contact.

I pulled over at the corner and sent two texts:

To: Mom and Dad. *Hi, arrived safely. Gram says hi and she looks good. On my way to Erin and Mary's. Love you.*
To: Harrison. *Hi, arrived safely. Saw my Gram from the driveway and she looks good. On my way to Erin and Mary's. How's it going?*

The return dings almost matched.

Mom and Dad: *Love you too. We're fine here. Stay Safe. XXXXOOO*

Harrison: *Miss you already. Nothing new here. There were two possible COVID-19 cases admitted today but no tests back yet. They were pretty sick anyway from other things. Both of them died. Tough conversations with the families because they couldn't visit. Take care of yourself, my Kit.*

I stared at the phone and felt a thrill. *My Kit.* Harrison was a true friend. And a truly good kisser.

Chapter Sixteen

"Don't let anyone treat you like an expired
24 butterfly gauge. You are a #16 in the left
forearm with excellent venous return!"
- Author unknown

My college suitemates Mary Talpin and Erin Mullen have lived together since graduation. They both work at TSU Hospital in different ICU step-down units. Somehow, they have been able to get full-time day-shift positions. The three of us just clicked in nursing school and have been close friends for over six years. When I told them that I was going to work at TSU Hospital until I was needed back at TMH, they begged me to stay with them. It was not a hard sell.

I made it to their townhouse around 6 pm. Last fall, they moved from a small two-bedroom apartment to this townhouse. It is such a sweet place with two bedrooms and two-and-a-half bathrooms and a little basement that they've painted and put down an IKEA rug, couch, and framed posters. Ta da! Now they have a "guest room/study room/I want to read while you watch TV room." There was no bed in the basement room, but plenty of space for my inflatable mattress.

Erin was home and came to the front door to help me carry in my stuff. She was the tallest and most elegant looking of the three of us. Her hair was naturally nearly platinum and worn in a braid wrapped around the nape of her neck. Her blue eyes and almost poreless skin worked together to create a perfect Irish colleen aura.

"Did I tell you I started powerlifting classes? They have helped so much," she began as she helped me carry in my stuff from the car. "They're on hold right now for the quarantine, of course, but the guy that teaches them is a friend of Matt. You know, Mary's Matt?"

Erin bent at the knees exhaled and pulled out my air mattress from the trunk in one smooth move.

I was in awe. My air mattress is the kind with a fold-out metal bed frame and comes in a suitcase. It weighs, if not a literal ton, then poundage very close to it.

"That weighs a ton!" I said not literally. "Seriously. Who is your weight guy?"

I followed behind her, hauling my backpack and iPad. I would have to come back for the rest since I didn't have the strength or the coordination of the new and stronger Erin.

"Kit, he is so smart and built. His name is Mark. He knows so much about physiology and nutrition and is a great teacher, too," she said, practically babbling. "He's friends with Matt. You remember Matt, right? He's a paramedic. Been really busy lately, but he's off tonight and he's coming over. Matt is coming over with Mark, I mean. You're going to love them. Wait until you see them side by side. Hunks of masculinity. They're in our COVID-19 social circle bubble. You'll get to see him a lot."

How long had it been since Erin and I talked, I wondered. This was close to TMI.

"I'm looking forward to staying with you guys," I said. "It's been a while since I've seen two hunks of masculinity. Side by side."

"You crack me up. I'm so glad you're here! I think I told you everything for now."

On our second trip to the car, Erin seemed to have taken a breath, so I let her know that nacho ingredients, including guacamole and Thompson's famous salsa, were in the back seat along with some wine coolers. I was glad to have some Thompson's Sassy Salsa in my cupboard since the small businesses were closed for the quarantine. I'd heard that the locally owned businesses in town were talking about offering online ordering and sharing delivery costs, but it hadn't started yet.

Mary was working until 7:30 pm and had asked us to make loaded nachos when she got home. I was glad I'd brought some chips, dip, salami, and cheese cubes, too. I was getting hungry and a little nervous about tomorrow. Snacks before nachos.

"Let's break open a wine cooler and some chips before the 3 Ms get here," I said.

"Matt and Mark and Mary," Erin laughed. "You're hilarious. I'm glad you're here."

No one could make me believe I'm as smart and funny and worthy as my closest friends. Mary and Erin were those kinds of friends for me. I felt like I'd come home.

"Me too," I said.

Chapter Seventeen

"Were there none who were discontented with what they have, the world would never reach anything better."
- Florence Nightingale

We heard Mary come home at 8 pm. She went straight to her room, and we saw her again at 8:20 pm, freshly showered and wearing a one-piece sweatshirt maxi dress. Her natural pixie afro framed exhausted-looking eyes.

"I've never been as paranoid about getting out of work clothes and into the shower as I have been the last three weeks," Mary said as she hugged me until I made a noise. "It's okay that we hug this one time. I just showered and looked away from you when I hugged."

"What is this? Are both of you in weight training?" I asked, rubbing my shoulder.

"Oh. My. Gosh. Yes! Did Erin tell you about Mark?"

"She mentioned something about him," I said, handing Mary a wine cooler. "What I can't get over is how you two are gushing over him. I cannot freakin' wait to lay eyes on him. And Matt, too, of course."

Mary was as raven as Erin is platinum. Her dad, Mitchell, was a history professor at TSU, and her mom, Aayla, was a translator for the state government. They met in Jamaica when Mary's dad was working on his doctoral dissertation. Over the course of a year, they married, and Mr. Talpin became Dr. Talpin. Mary was an only child and speaks English, French, and Spanish with ease. You would think Mary would be spoiled and entitled and act like what she is: the only princess of two accomplished parents. She was not. Mary Talpin was a caring, open, and humble human being. I was proud to call her my dear friend.

"Oh, Kit," she said. "The group you're going to work with is a godsend. The proning team is giving us the help we need to position our COVID-19 patients. This whole thing is a nightmare. Our patients come in looking pretty good. We put a pulse oximeter on them expecting oxygen readings in the 90s. Nope— they have readings in the resuscitation range. Honestly, they will be talking to you, even getting up and moving in the room, and yet have oxygen levels in the 40s. Sometimes we can get their levels up to the 80s or low 90s with oxygen. Then, within a few hours, they're in full respiratory failure and heading toward kidney, liver, and lung shutdown. In the last two days, every one of my patients died. I'm glad to be off for a couple of days."

"It's not like we aren't used to working hard," Erin said. "We stayed in motion all day when things were normal pre-COVID. This is a whole different level of hard work. It's like nightmare-hard labor. There is really no treatment yet; it's supportive nursing care and oxygen. The infectious disease and respiratory physicians are trying some things, but nothing works very well. If you have COVID-19, you have a 50:50 chance of getting out of the hospital alive. Half are dying."

"And the equipment we have to wear!" Mary groaned. "That makes it ten times worse. Staffing is so short. We're getting called in every time we sign up for mandatory on-call."

I was beginning to seriously question my decision to work at TSUH when I heard a sharp three-tap knock at the door.

Erin jumped up and walk-ran to the door. I looked at Mary and she grinned, rolling her eyes. "The woman is smitten, I fear," she said.

Matt came in first and held out a fist bump for me. I had only heard about him, but Mary's taste in men remained stellar. Matt was a tall lean Black man with broad shoulders and deltoid muscles that strained his t-shirt. He smiled as though the only thing he ever wanted to do was to come over tonight for nachos and our company. The words that came to mind were "such a nice guy."

Behind him was a guy with a Marine-style haircut wearing tight running pants and a workout spandex shirt. Part of a tattoo showed over his left deltoid. He was smiling in an ultra-self-confident sort of way. The words that came to mind were "narcissistic jerk."

"Hi, I'm Mark," he said.

"I'm Kit," I said.

"Kinda figured that you know," Mark smirked. "Mary, Erin, Matt, me. You're the odd guy out."

"And you're the pinnacle of social grace," I said before thinking.

The pinnacle of his intelligence must not have included big words because Mark ignored my comment and zeroed in on our chips, dip, and salami.

"Tell me you're not eating cured meat," he said. "Feel like dying soon, do you?"

"Oh Mark, don't be silly," said Erin. "Kit brought it from Thompson."

Way to throw me to the wolves, I thought.

"Mark is a pescetarian," Erin said by way of explanation.

"That means I'm a vegetarian but will eat fish for the omega 3, protein, and B12 value it brings to my diet," he said. "*Pesce* is Italian for fish."

"Buono," I said.

"Haha. You tried to answer me in Italian," he said. "I like you. Hey, listen, don't feel bad about being from Thompson. My grandparents are from there and their diet is full of sugar and fat. So, I get it."

This guy was a real piece of work. "Nachos anyone?" I asked. "Only cheese, tomatoes, olives, and guac. No meat or fish, cured or otherwise."

That changed the subject and awkwardness. The nachos were fantastic, and Sassy Salsa didn't fail to impress. I didn't offer my sugar, full-fat sour cream, and flour-laden Irish soda bread.

The next hour went by amicably. Matt talked a little about the concerns he had with transporting so many possible COVID-19 patients in his EMS runs. Protective equipment was in short supply everywhere, so the paramedics were double-gloving, and wearing an N95 and a wrap-around eye shield during the whole shift. Between patients, hand hygiene was strenuously enforced, but protecting clothing from secretions was difficult. So far, disposable isolation gowns were the only thing available. Matt wasn't sure how long the supply would last.

I was learning so much, and yet felt less well informed about COVID-19 than when I'd arrived.

Mark was planning to make YouTube exercise and weight-lifting videos during the quarantine. His goal was to stay productive and keep his clients loyal to his services. That actually made some sense.

My phone told me it was time for me to wrap this up. "It's 10:00," I said. "I need to shower and get to bed. The alarm goes off at 5:45 am for my first day and orientation."

Mary looked at me with sleepy gratitude, so I waved goodnight, went to the basement to inflate my bed, and got my thoughts together.

Chapter Eighteen

"We must be learning all our lives."
- Florence Nightingale

After my shower and making my bed, I realized I needed my Sip and Stitch friends. These wonderful women—and one man—helped me survive the first six months of being an RN. That time in nurse residency nearly killed me. Sip and Stitch helped me figure out how to stay sane and translate ideas like compassion and empathy into top-notch nursing care.

We'd all worked on 3 North at TMH and met once a month at someone's house/apartment/manufactured home. We brought whatever craft project we were working on, shared snacks, brought our own drinks, and talked about things only another nurse could appreciate. I usually brought my current quilting project, cheeses, wine coolers, and at least one question for these more experienced nurses.

During quarantine, we started a private social media group. My iPad opened right up to the site.

Kit: Hi, I really missed you tonight. The drive to San Davers was OK but the roads are practically deserted. Erin and Mary's new place is really nice. Since the place has a little finished basement, I have my own space and don't have to sleep in their living room. We had a nacho party after Mary got home from work and the guy Mary is seeing came over with his friend.

Matt, Mary's guy, is a nice and super smart EMT.

His friend is a weightlifting "lifestyle coach." (I did not make that up. That's how he described his job.) His name is Mark, and his entire brain is filled with self-affirming messages. Mark is a Grade-A jerk, but I've got three brothers, so I was no match for him. He was just annoying, like a fly that you just can't get with the flyswatter. Boring. He loves to explain… Tala calls it mansplaining, you know? It's almost as though he's pretty darn sure I won't understand the intricacies of whatever complex idea he's talking about. Here's a breathtaking example: "Did you know that if you have a wide stance (that's when you place your legs farther apart) and bend your knees before lifting something heavy, your quads (those are muscles in your upper leg) will help you lift and save your thoracic and lumbar muscles (those are in your back)?" It was all I could do not to bat my eyes and say "Oh my gosh, Sherlock. That is so fascinating. As a nurse, I've never heard of such a thing. Could you go over that complicated idea one more time?" (Hey Tala: See? I'm getting more language-creative every day this pandemic goes on.)

Get this: he has a tattoo on his almost-steroid-powered musculus deltoideus. That's a muscle on your upper arm (OK, I'll try to stop Kit-splaining). It's just that he seemed convinced he'd written Gray's Anatomy (the book, not the show).

I hope you're sitting down.

The tattoo is **C10H12N5O13P3-4.** Do you know what that is? It's ATP! Or as Mark said in an ultra-serious tone as he nodded encouragingly and scanned the room for others who could benefit from his command of chemistry, "It's ATP, which is short for adenosine triphosphate. ATP is a small molecule that does a very important job: it carries energy for all the cells in the body." I'M NOT KIDDING. HE ACTUALLY SAID THAT TO THREE NURSES AND AN EMT! My apologies for all caps, but really?

Do you believe such arrogance? Did anyone tell him what we do for a living? I could tell he was gearing up to review the steps of the Kreb's cycle (the bunch of chemical reactions where the cell makes this ATP stuff…you know). I wanted to bat my eyelashes and say to him, "Oh, Mark, you are just so smart. It seems to me that the Kreb's cycle was covered in nursing school. The first year. First semester." Instead, I jumped up to get more salsa.

But Matt is nice and smart and hunky. He has the kind of muscles that come from real work, not just lifting dumbbells (get it? Dumb Bells? Mark?) Matt clearly likes Mary, and I was fascinated by his EMS stories. Apparently, these two dudes are part of our social bubble. Stay tuned for more fascinating accounts of muscle cellular activity.

Oh. My. Gosh. It was the EMS and hospital stories about COVID that got me. Matt talked about how people looked when he took them to the hospital, and Erin and Mary picked up with nursing stories. COVID-19 is killing almost everyone who goes on a ventilator. It sounds like anyone with preexisting conditions is doomed. They said people with diabetes, obesity, and cardiac disease go downhill the fastest. They had one healthy TSU student who came to the ER and died in 2 days. One of the ICU nurses got COVID-19, and she is still at home on oxygen.

Tomorrow, I'll see for myself. It's the orientation to the proning practice at TMU, and then on to the units with the day-shift team. Thanks for listening to me. Later.

PS: How's the furlough going? Has anybody been called back in the 10 hours since I left town?

Tala: I'm proud of your language development. I think you like Mark. He sounds like an ass—and that's not swearing. It's an animal found in the Bible. Check it out.

Patrick: I can't stop laughing. Are you f—ing kidding me? ATP? My faculty colleagues at the community college will be rolling on the floor with that tattoo story.

Tala: I'm going to work with the Sisters of the Angels and Cherubim at my college. Just until the end of the furlough.

They have a transition facility for ill and declining sisters. There is never enough help in the extended care section, so they said they'd pay me and let me stay in guest rooms at the convent. My job will be working on their quality reports to the diocese funding group and helping the CNAs improve their body mechanics with the sicker sisters.

Barb: I'm glad you're safe, Kit. You'll be fine tomorrow. It sounds like this Mark really got under your skin. Tala, that sounds like important work.

Rosie: You're going to live in a convent, Tala? That gave me the best laugh! Maybe the sisters can get your language under control.

Tala: Haha. Not in the convent! In the guest rooms. Listen, my SAC sisters aren't as naïve as you might think. I'm sure they will appreciate most of my language. Probably.

Susan: Kit, you sound like you're half in love with Mark...I'm so glad you're still up. This furlough stinks. I still can't sleep at night, and I needed a laugh. Thanks to both you and Tala! A convent! An ATP tattoo! I hope we can keep COVID out of Thompson. I heard there was possibly an admission with COVID today, but the person died, and the test won't be back for a few days.

Kit: Get this. According to Mr. Muscle Energy, Thompson is full of fat people who wouldn't recognize a green vegetable unless it was drowned in butter. That's based on some family from Thompson. He feels bad for me that I'm stuck there.

Rosie: You crack me up! Mark sounds like he could be a late-night cable TV star. I agree with Susan. You're way too upset with him. I think you like him. When did you ever care what people thought of Thompson? Good luck tomorrow.

Tala: Be sure your eyebrows look good tomorrow. That's what everyone will see when you put on the mask.

Barb: Wear your daily contacts tomorrow and throw them away after work. You won't be able to put on and take off your glasses while wearing all that gear.

Susan: Barb's right. I know we aren't supposed to know you need glasses sometimes, but wear your contacts, my sometimes-vain friend. The glasses will fog up with the mask.

Tala: If you didn't live in that fancy apartment, you could have had Lasik by now and not need glasses.

Kit: Leave my very chic Chateau Bordeaux apartment out of this! Did you really know about my glasses?

Rosie: You're kidding, right? Yes, Kit, we're onto your corrective lenses' secret.

Patrick: I have to sign off now. My eyebrow tweezers are calling me.

Kit: Love you guys. 'Night.

Susan: Me too.

Barb: Good night kiddo. Good night, Sister Tala!

Rosie: Sleep well. Let us know about tomorrow.

I closed out and fell immediately to sleep.

Chapter Nineteen

"Let whoever is in charge keep this simple question in her head (not, how can I always do this right thing myself, but) how can I provide for this right thing to be always done?"
- Florence Nightingale

I got myself to the proning orientation at 6:35 am. Thank heavens I attended school on that complex, or I would have been lost trying to read the little map and locate the best parking garage and the correct entrance.

Orientation was in Building G, mezzanine level. There were disposable surgical masks at the door. A masked person handed me a mask and hand sanitizer. I put on the mask as I made my way to the most important part of the room. Individually wrapped bagels, cream cheese, donuts, fruit cups, juice boxes, tea, and coffee were provided. Open buffets were a thing of the past.

If being a hospital nurse has taught me anything, it is to grab food when you can because when patient care gets busy, you don't know when you'll get another chance. Plus, this was free. You don't get much free food at hospitals anymore.

"Well, I'll be dipped in sh—sugar water," said a familiar voice.

"Tala! What are you doing here?" I asked in surprise, grabbing my bagel before it dropped to the floor.

"Well, my SAC sisters made a deal with TMU to send me here so I can teach the CNAs how to prone the sick sisters with respiratory issues. I won't go on the floors with you after lunch, so just this morning."

"It's wonderful to see you! They just gave us a paper surgical mask. They said they'd give us an N95 when we got here. I don't know anything else, do you? This is so crazy," I jabbered.

"I'm glad to be here too," Tala said. "Kit, I'm beginning to think that this COVID-19 is no joke. Not that I didn't know it was a bad virus, but for the love of all the saints, this is like a baptism of fire."

I stared at her. Two church references in one sentence without one swear word. How long had she been hanging around those nuns? I wondered.

"Anyway, you don't look at all stressed," I said. "I'd like to look as cool and in control, as you do."

"Oh yeah, cool on the outside and like a squirrel in rush hour traffic on the inside," Tala laughed. "When I worked on the reservation after graduation, I learned really quick how to look calm and unruffled, no matter what."

"Let's get started," said a voice from the front of the room. "Please sit at least six feet apart, that's every fourth chair."

Tala and I moved apart.

"My name is Liz and I'm from the Infection Control Department at TSUH. Thank you all for coming today. Your temporary positions here are particularly important to support our nurses on the COVID-19 units. Let's take a couple of minutes to introduce ourselves. Could you please stand, keep your mask on, and introduce yourself? Your name, your title, and where you're from. This will be good practice in speaking through a mask and listening to your colleagues wearing masks."

There were nine of us in the room. Eight of us were going to be prone team members, half on nights and half on days. Six of us were RNs, and two were physical therapists. We all came from community hospitals in the TSU health system. Tala was an RN but only here as a guest.

It took careful listening to hear names. I know I didn't catch everything said. This was the first time I really began to understand the problem of listening to a muffled voice behind a mask without the benefit of seeing facial expressions. A new skill set to convey emotion and information between colleagues and patients would be needed.

"Thanks, everyone," said Liz. "It was hard to understand each other, right? You'll get better at it, and we hope that some of the things we'll tell you about today will be helpful, too."

Liz held up a large, laminated sign that said "LIZ, RN" in large print with her picture under it. "You'll each get your picture taken without a mask, and before you leave this morning, you'll have your own sign. We'll show you how to attach it to a gown or scrubs, so no matter whether you're in a patient room or someplace else in the hospital, people will know what you look like. We are committed to providing as much human touch as possible during the pandemic. You'll be wearing a mask and your sign at all times in the hospital. Okay?"

No one spoke and we all nodded.

"On the hospital units, you will wear a hospital-issue N95 mask at all times. You'll leave the mask here when you go home. When you come in, you must wear a paper or cloth mask or grab one at the employee entrance. You'll use that mask when leaving the hospital and until you get to your car. Once you get to your work setting, your N95 mask will go on. Questions?"

No one spoke and we all nodded.

"Okay," said Liz. "Let's get you all measured for your N95 masks. Listen, I know they're supposed to be used for one patient only and then discarded. But we don't have that luxury. There is not a stockpile of masks nationwide anymore, and presently, we are short of enough N95 masks to follow the best standard of care." She went on, "Neither do we have enough isolation gowns to use only once. As nurses, we are accustomed to figuring out ways to creatively work around challenges. I know you all will make the best of this, so we keep each other and our patients safe. Any questions?"

A few nurses expressed very legitimate concern about reusing N95 masks and isolation gowns. It was still shocking to me that the federal stockpile of emergency equipment had vanished.

"Great. Thanks. Now let's talk proning," said Liz.

"Boy, has she bought the party line," whispered Tala. "What the actual fu..frog is this? She's acting like it's no big deal to say, "We can't protect you from this super contagious disease, but we have exceptionally fine lunch bags to clean up your contaminated masks while you're not at work. Yes, this is a disease so contagious that extra negative airflow rooms were installed in all our hospitals, but you nurses are used to working in dangerous situations, so it'll be fine. Trust me. It's OK. You're just nurses.'"

"I know what you mean," I whispered. "They may be able to plead ignorance about the virus, but we do know that N95 masks aren't meant to be worn for hours at a time. Our wet breath is enough to break down the filtration effectiveness. I feel like I'm in a third-world country getting by with a measly supply donated by some charity group."

"Well, lick a duck," said Tala. "Did you love that pretend swearing?"

I snorted which I tried to cover with a cough. Liz glanced over at us.

"I love you, Tala," I said. "I'm glad everybody's getting face shields, too. Will you get them too at SAC?"

Tala nodded, poked my side, and gestured to look ahead at Liz.

I glanced over and saw Tala wearing her "I can't believe what you're saying, it is so incredibly fascinating" look. Reining in my laughter on the inside and looking seriously attentive on the outside, I tuned in back to Liz.

For the next 30 minutes, the proning procedure was demonstrated in a video.

Here was the information in a truly concise nutshell:

> Proning means placing a patient from
> their back to their belly. The technique has
> been around for a while and has been shown
> to improve oxygenation when patients have
> respiratory distress. Proning is effective with
> COVID-19 patients. It helps ease the struggle
> to breathe. Proning can prevent the need for
> a ventilator.
>
> It takes at least five skilled caregivers to
> turn a patient from supine to a prone position.
> That's two on each side of the bed and one at
> the head to watch the oxygen tubing and the
> person's airway.

We took a short break and Liz pulled back a room divider
to reveal a hospital bed with a mannequin connected to two IVs,
a Foley urine catheter, and an oxygen mask.

I could see that Liz was a superb example of how good
continuing education nurses think. She loved lists, especially if
they came with step-by-step instructions. There was a right way
and a wrong way, by golly, and she's going to show us! Here was
the bottom line: nurses learn to make important technical skills
a habit. If we don't have to think about every step every time,
there was less chance that we would screw up by missing a step
and hurting a patient, or ourselves.

Here were the four skills we needed to master before lunch.

1. *Don and Doff PPE in the correct order. That means
   putting on and taking off the personal protective
   equipment needed to go into a person's room who has
   COVID-19. The correct order is really important, too,*

because if done incorrectly, we could contaminate ourselves or others.

2. *Turn a patient (the mannequin) from supine (back) to prone (belly) position.*

3. *Demonstrate to a TSUH Nursing Continuing Education Department nurse that we can do #1 and #2 correctly. Twice.*

4. *Bring up our Employee Continuing Education link on the TSU website and get a sign-off from that nurse.*

5. *Once we've completed #4, we could go to lunch and meet on the unit at 1300 hours. That's 1:00 pm.*

"Ready?" asked Liz.

No one spoke and we all nodded.

Then, four people walked in wearing full PPE: gown, N95 mask, eye shield, and double-gloved. They walked in together, and they looked just like the Ghostbusters. Who you gonna call? Prone team!

Chapter Twenty

"Until you're ready to look foolish, you'll never have the possibility of being great."

- Cher

We were divided into our team groups for the picture-taking, PPE, and patient-proning sections of the morning. There were four of us in my group. We would be assigned to work three 12-hour night shifts each week, and an extra four hours on another night shift to equal 40 hours per week. In this way, the units had improved staffing schedules and the hospital wouldn't have to pay overtime. I was familiar with this way of scheduling since we had been doing something similar with on-call hours at TMH for over a year. We would work together until the community TSU hospitals called back the furloughed nurses. On the day of orientation, they thought it would be about five weeks until that happened.

My group was Jackie, an RN from Lakeside General, a small TSU hospital west of San Davers; Joan, an RN from Sutter Memorial, a TSU hospital east of San Davers; and Ken, a physical therapist (PT), also from Sutter.

Each time we turned a patient, we would have a nurse or respiratory therapist from the nursing unit help us. They would make the fifth person. If possible, other staff would help as well since five is the minimum number to safely prone a patient in severe respiratory distress.

I thought my picture turned out pretty well. Usually, "official pictures" don't flatter me. I tend to look like I'm being forced to smile with a gun to my back. Self-congratulations aside, I really appreciated the idea of patients and colleagues being able to see our faces without a mask or goggles, or face shield.

After attaching our pictures to our scrubs, we stood in a group, waiting for our chance to practice donning and doffing the PPE. There was a way to do this without contaminating yourself. Jackie had this brilliant idea to help us remember the right order. She was the quietest one in our group but quite the practical thinker. Here was her idea:

When putting on PPE, think of the way you get ready for work in the morning: shower (hand washing, or at the very least, hand sanitizer), put on your scrubs (gown), lipstick or aftershave (mask), sunglasses (goggles or face shield), and car keys in hand (gloves). PPE should be removed in alphabetical order (gloves, goggles, gown, and mask, then wash hands.)

Joan, the most outgoing in our group, tried to set the process to music. She sang a song from the kids' show *Happy Socks*, "This is the way we wash our hands, wash our hands, wash our hands, this is the way we wash our hands early every morning. This is the way we put on our gown, put on our gown" … you get the picture. Yes, she had little kids, and yes, that seemed to have affected her higher cognitive functioning.

Ken rolled his eyes and said, "I should have taken that early retirement package last year."

The music was short-lived. Joan could take a hint.

In spite of the musical detour, we all learned Jackie's technique and passed the donning and doffing test in under 15 minutes.

Next was the turning station. Each person on the team had a position and a job to do at that position. The person at the head was in charge of watching the oxygen equipment and making sure the patient's neck was straight to keep the airway open.

A respiratory therapist (RT) or RN was in the head position. Always.

The nurses and therapists on the sides of the bed do the rolling and positioning from back to stomach, and then, 16 to 18 hours later, stomach to back. This wasn't too hard for me since turning and positioning are part of clinical fundamentals in nursing, and I practiced it frequently on 3 North. Turning a patient all the way to the belly was a new additional step, but the technique was familiar. We focused on smooth coordination of each step with four other people, watching all the equipment lines and tubing so that it didn't become tangled or disconnected.

Proning worked because the largest air exchange in the lungs occurs from the posterior (back) side and at the bases (the bottom of the lungs.) Proning takes the pressure of the mattress off the diaphragm, internal organs, and posterior lungs, which is how it helps lung expansion.

The mannequin was state-of-the-art. If we accidentally did something that would compromise the airway, pulled out a piece of equipment, or even just pinched off some equipment, the alarm would sound. There was no mistaking the alarm, either. It was like playing the game Operation, except the alarm wouldn't shut up. It was loud and persisted until the problem was fixed. Turning and proning a person was trickier than it looked and took a least 30 minutes to do it safely and correctly.

After Liz recorded our completion, it was 11:45 am. We had 75 minutes for lunch—an unheard-of luxury. Tala had also finished and came over to our group.

Ken cleared his throat. "Could I ask you something?" he asked. "I knew this was serious before this morning. But since we haven't seen any COVID-19 cases in Sutter, I didn't realize how much nursing and physical therapy were necessary just to keep people breathing." He paused and looked down. "Would any of you mind if we met together as a team a couple of minutes before Shift Report every night and had a short prayer or moment of silence? I feel like I need to make sure we are all together before we stay masked, gowned, and gloved for over 12 hours. What do you think?"

We all looked at each other. No one wanted to talk first. We didn't know each other at all and didn't want to say the wrong thing about something so personal.

"Excuse me, sorry to butt in. I'm Tala and I'm only here for the morning. While on furlough from Thompson, I'm working at the Sisters of Angels and Cherubim in their extended care facility. We always begin each shift with a short prayer or psalm and a minute of silence. I'm a little over the top sometimes—just ask Kit—but honestly? It makes me feel the spirit of nursing."

I could have hugged her, except for the social distancing thing. Jackie and Joan interrupted each other all at once to agree Ken's idea was an incredibly good one. From behind our masks, I saw our eyes reflect smiles of relief.

Tala had to return to the convent, and my group had our packed lunches to eat. We gave each other fist bumps and set off trying to find a place where we could eat at least six feet apart and not get into anyone's way at the immense TSUH health care complex.

The morning was over. I knew this was the easy part. I sent a quick plea to heaven that my movements would be as smooth with patients as they'd been with the mannequin.

Chapter Twenty-One

"The most important practical lesson that can be given to nurses is to teach them what to observe-how to observe-what symptoms indicate improvement-what the reverse-which are of importance-which are of none-which are the evidence of neglect -and of what kind of neglect."
- Florence Nightingale

Jackie, Joan, Ken, and I made our way to Building D, 6 Southeast, our assigned intensive care step down unit. We were told to report to Max, the charge nurse. While I looked around for a male nurse, a tall woman with a pink-tipped ponytail looked up from her TIMES screen.

"Hi, I'm Max, or Maxine or you prefer," she said. "We're glad to have you here. Let me find Rob, your coordinator. It's time for the afternoon turns and we need you to get started. Wait here."

We stood in a line against the wall and smiled at another masked face wearing a "Kathy, RN" picture on her scrubs.

"Well," she said with a sniff that was audible through the mask. "We must be in serious trouble if they're bringing people from Band-Aid Station General Hospital to help us."

"I'm sorry?" asked Joan.

"I can understand that you'd think you can be a nurse in the big city, but I'm afraid that you're not used to the kinds of patients we have here. Just try not to get in our way or hurt somebody," she said, turning away.

"That's a pile of crap," said Joan, growling behind her mask.

"Don't listen to her," I said to my group. "I went to school here and some nurses believe that any nurse who doesn't work in the big university hospital setting is clueless about quality or complicated nursing care." Remembering the first days of my nurse residency, I continued, "When I went to work in Thompson, I thought I was going to Easy Street Hospital. The first week—heck the first day—nearly killed me!"

"Just ignore it," Ken agreed. "But we aren't on top of their routine here and have to learn that. Let's just concentrate on the principles of proning and taking care of the patients."

"Stop it, Kathy," said a male voice. "We're lucky to have these nurses and therapists. Hi, I'm Rob. I'm the RT on the night proning team. We will see one another's eyes quite a bit for the next few days or weeks."

"Thanks, Rob," said Maxine to our respiratory therapist. "Honestly, Kathy! Band-Aid stations?"

Rob's gray-brown eyebrows relaxed, and he turned to us. "It's nice to meet you Ken, Jackie, Kit, and Joan," he said, reading our signs. "C'mon over to the alcove and let's get going." After we joined him at the alcove, he continued. "Just to clarify, I'm usually on nights, and so are you. After today, we will work as a five-person team. I'm here today in the middle of my sleep cycle, as you know, to get us started. We aren't working tonight, of course, but we'll meet in the Shift Report room tomorrow night. We will all work the same shifts, including the extra four hours each week. Questions?"

"Yes," I said. "So, we're working tomorrow night, right? Do you have our schedule?"

"Yep," said Rob. "We will work from 7 pm to 7 am tomorrow. We will then be off one night, then on from midnight to 4 am the next night, and then off one night, then on two nights and off two nights, and then repeat. You should find the schedule on your TSU employee portal. The final team schedule was approved this morning. Okay?"

We all nodded, and Ken gave a thumbs-up. This was more like it. I could understand the schedule. Next stop: patient care.

Rob nodded. "Before we go into any patient's room, we will review the patient's name and any pertinent information we've received from Shift Report. Max filled me in on the five patients we are scheduled to turn in the next six hours. Okay?

"Our first patient is Ms. Ruth Gazelle. She is a 67-year-old woman with chronic lung disease and a history of congestive heart failure. We don't have her COVID-19 test results yet, but she presented with symptoms we're coming to recognize… fever, cough, and a pulse oximeter reading of 60. Of course, she was placed on high-flow O2 by mask and that brought her pulse ox up to the 90s. But after a few hours, she started to decompensate, and her readings dropped. Ms. Gazelle is somewhat obese—not huge but has a large belly. The decision was made to use proning to hopefully avoid needing a ventilator. It worked yesterday. She's been in supine position since 6 and now it's time to get her off her back. Okay? Let's go.

"And BTW." His eyes crinkled as though he was smiling, "You'll be fine. I'll be at the head of the bed always. Today, you each will take a different spot on the sides of the bed to get used to each position."

I understood that the reason Rob was always at the head of the bed was because airway management was primary. A respiratory therapist or ICU nurse would always be monitoring the airway. If the patient didn't tolerate turning, Rob would direct us to pause, speed up, or reverse the process while monitoring mask placement, and closed connections of oxygen tubing, pulse ox, respiratory rate, color, facial expressions, and other signs of oxygenation.

Proning wasn't as easy as flipping a person from their back to their belly. Life-preserving medical equipment needed to be considered, and individual patient reactions to proning weren't always instantly positive.

Rob led the way to Ms. Gazelle's room. We took turns in the anteroom, changing into a gown, face shield, and gloves. We placed our name signs from scrubs to gowns.

Rob caught Ms. Gazelle's eyes and moved to touch her hands. "Ms. Gazelle? I'm Rob, the respiratory therapist. My team and I are here to turn you on your belly and give you some breathing relief. Is that all right with you?"

She nodded.

"Would you like us to call you Ms. Gazelle?"

The patient shook her head.

"Ruth?"

She nodded.

"That's great, Ruth. This is Ken, Joan, Jackie, and Kit. They're nurses and a physical therapist. Together, we will help you turn."

We each took a spot on the side of the bed, which was moved to a higher position. Ruth had been grasping the upper side rails to straighten her chest. This was a compensatory position to help her get more air by expanding her chest.

Rob and Ruth worked to arrange her oxygen mask for the move. Jackie and Joan were at the bottom sides of the bed. They made sure the Foley catheter tubing was arranged and Ruth's elastic stockings were straightened. The alternating pressure mattress was checked for proper inflation to avoid pressure on Ruth's knees and hips after turning.

Ken and I were at the top of the bed. We made sure the tubing from both IVs was smooth and extra tubing was positioned to avoid pulling during the turn. Ken and I slowly released Ruth's hands and lowered the upper side rails.

Rob quietly called out each step of the procedure. After making sure the mask and all the tubes were secured, Ruth's head was placed flat, and the top sheet was moved up to Ruth's thighs.

At Rob's command, "Turn," she was turned toward Jackie and me. Her bottom sheet was straightened, and the absorbent pad changed. Rob noted out loud Ruth's pulse ox reading and cardiac rhythm.

"Are you OK, Ruth?' he asked. She nodded.

Jackie and I checked the position of the tubing, Ruth's lower extremities, and oxygen mask.

"Clear," we said in unison to Rob.

I looked down at Ruth. Her brow was furrowed, and her eyes bore into mine.

I placed my gloved hand over her upper arm and said, "I'm Kit the nurse. You're doing well." Her shoulders relaxed with a sigh.

"Ready?" asked Rob.

"Yes," we said.

"Here we go, Ruth. Roll please," directed Rob.

Ruth was placed in prone position. Rob placed Ruth's head in a foam head support device while simultaneously checking her airway. The mask was repositioned, and he placed EKG monitor pads on her back. Ken and I positioned Ruth's arms in a "swimming" position, bent at the elbow and above her head, to make the chest expansion as full as possible.

Ruth's pulse ox moved from 85 to 94 and her cardiac monitor showed regular sinus rhythm at 73 beats per minute.

"Lines and tubing check," said Rob. We verified everything was connected and functioning.

The final step was supporting her hips and legs with bolsters and slightly raising her head while marginally lowering her legs. This was called the Reverse Trendelenburg position.

"Okay, Ruth?" asked Rob.

She shrugged.

"We're going to stay here for a couple of minutes to be sure everything is going well," Rob said. "I'm going to talk to the team to be sure we're all watching out for you."

He turned to us. "Respiratory rate, respiratory effort, pulse ox, EKG rhythm, eyes protected, and double tubing check... okay?"

We folded our gloved hands in front of our gowns and observed. It was amazing to see how effectively proning worked. By taking mattress pressure off the diaphragm, belly, and internal organs, the posterior lungs had less resistance to expand. Ruth's depth of breathing changed. It was obvious she was more relaxed. Her pulse ox was 95 now.

I watched the clock on the wall. After five full minutes, Rob spoke again, "And most importantly, how are you doing, Ruth?"

"Thank you. Better, it's better," she said.

Rob leaned toward Ruth's face, lightly touching her shoulder, and said, "Thank you for helping us. Rest now, OK?"

We moved to the anteroom and removed our PPE in the correct order. Because of supply scarcity, our now-contaminated gowns were hung on door hooks rather than discarded. I was the last one out of the room and shut the door firmly to preserve the negative airflow in Ruth's room.

While washing my hands, I glanced at my watch. We had been with Ruth for 45 minutes.

Chapter Twenty-Two

"The individual registered nurse should remain
focused on patients and is responsible for giving the
best possible care under the circumstances."
- American Nurses Association 2020

The rest of the first day and subsequent night shifts went by in a blur. We never stopped moving from patient to patient. Some were placed prone, and others were placed supine. The preferred routine was 18 hours prone and 6 hours supine. Truthfully, we were thrilled if the patient was around the next shift so we could repeat the proning routine.

COVID-19 was so unpredictable that during the remainder of March and into early April, we rarely had the same patients to turn from night to night. Of the seven to ten patients we turned in each night, about half were not on the next shift I worked. Most patients went to the highest-level ICU setting for ventilator placement. About two in ten patients were not able to be ventilated. COVID-19 infections progressed so rapidly that kidney, liver, and lung failure commonly led to death within hours. Those who were placed on ventilators almost all died. The impact of COVID-19 on the lungs seemed unstoppable.

Ruth Gazelle was one of those patients. By 10 pm that evening, she had a respiratory arrest while in prone position. She was resuscitated, intubated, and placed on a ventilator. Ruth died the next morning from overwhelming pneumonia.

While at work, there was no time to grieve or even begin to realize the extent of the horror we were seeing. If we weren't turning patients, we were helping other nurses. If we were not in a patient room and a nurse was occupied with a Code Blue (cardiac/respiratory arrest), the prone team kept an eye on their four or five other patients.

Rob tried to assure that we each got two 15 to 20-minute breaks in our 12-hour shift. The weather was becoming more spring-like, so I would take a water bottle, guzzle it, grab another bottle, and head outside for ten minutes of mask-free air. I began bringing quick things to eat. Granola bars, high protein bars, and my homemade bread with peanut butter and jelly were my go-to foods. If I had water and some food with protein and carbohydrates, I could stay alert and strong for the next six hours. A quick bathroom break, and I was back on the unit in about 20 minutes.

Even before I came to the prone team, I realized that camaraderie or teamwork could make or break my attitude at work. I didn't know how I would have survived these nights without Ken, Jackie, Joan, and Rob. We never complained, and we had each other's back. The empathy we shared through our eyes and eyebrows was lifesaving.

Here's an example: when a nurse or therapist was at the head of the bed during the turn, the patient's face and eyes spoke volumes. Sometimes the fear, resignation, or simply the need to feel loved and respected came through so forcefully. For that reason, we usually changed places between patients at the top and bottom of the bed. Emotional overload was an ever-present threat.

I was never sure if what I said to patients was helpful or not. I knew it was hard to convey empathy with just my eyes. I found that even when I was wearing gloves if I touched a patient's arm or hands, the patient held my eyes. I used phrases such as "I'm here," "My name is Kit and I'm a nurse," "We've got you," and "It's going to be okay."

Using the person's name was especially important. If our patient was conscious, we always started our conversation by learning their preferred name. A few patients who recovered told me they knew we understood when we told them, "Everything will work out." There was no sugar-coating the facts; this was a terrible time for them. We knew they understood how sick they were. But we were here with them. We wanted them to know we had hope that everything would work out.

I didn't know how Rob managed to stay so focused and supportive. He was looking into each and every patient's eyes every time. On one occasion, he and I had a break at the same time. He grabbed his water and a donut and waved to me as he walked straight to the chapel.

Chapter Twenty-Three

"United States leads the world in COVID19 cases, with
cases topping 81,000 and deaths topping 1,000."
- Donald G. McNeil, Jr., The New York Times, 3/26/2020

The rate of contagion and death toll continued to rise in the weeks leading up to Easter. We had been told COVID-19 would be a bad memory and churches would be filled when the Christian church's most important holiday rolled around.

From where I stood wrapped in PPE, it seemed it would take a miracle rivaling the Resurrection for COVID-19 cases to disappear or even diminish by April 12th. The number of known COVID-19 cases was sobering enough, but I wondered, what about those cases that were not identified because of mild symptoms or lack of dependable and quick testing materials? The chance of those people spreading the virus was completely unknown, but I'd bet was pretty darn high.

It was true that our patients who died were mainly those persons who had other serious chronic illnesses, but there were a few otherwise healthy younger people who we repositioned every night. By the Monday before Easter Sunday, our proning team had cared for six under 50-year-old patients who did not have poor health before COVID-19. Every one of them died.

The San Davers community rallied around the hospital staff. Outside the hospital walls, there were banners everywhere. "We Love Nurses!" "TSUH Nurses Are Our Heroes!" "We Are Grateful to Doctors and Nurses!"

No one who was not a patient or a staff member was allowed into the hospital buildings. No exceptions. Food donations for hospital staff were dropped off at the security gates and guards carried them to the hospital buildings. Sometimes one of the 6 Southeast staff would make a run to the Building D front desk and bring back cookies or cold pizza or sub sandwiches. When cola and other sodas were delivered, we emptied those 2-liter bottles in a flash. There was nothing like the rush of sugar found in a soda, especially if that soda also contained caffeine. We would walk over to the windowsill where lunch bags kept our N95 masks until the next shift or until they tore or were damaged. Standing a good distance apart, we'd lower our masks and eat as fast as we could.

I especially remember a couple of very hard nights. On one shift, three of my patients died in six hours. I was stunned at the loss of life and flat-out astonished at how quickly COVID-19 killed. There was nothing medically that could be done to prevent or treat body systems collapse. The only tools we had were impeccable nursing care. We positioned bodies, supported the airway, and hydration balance, and tried to instill hope.

The memory of some patients still sticks with me. Jack O'Rourke was one of those patients.

Jack was a 42-year-old small business owner in San Davers. He and his husband Kevin Finnegan were married two months before Jack developed a fever, a severe headache, and difficulty breathing. Kevin was a successful real estate agent in San Davers. Kevin loved billboard advertising, so his face was known all over town.

Jack was admitted to D-6 Southeast around 10:30 pm. Since the unit was one RN short, I volunteered to admit him from the Emergency Department. Our team had 30 minutes to spare until the next proning time slot.

I learned a lot about Jack and Kevin without much probing. They were ready to go to Ireland for a honeymoon when all international travel was shut down. Jack said, "Where else would two Irish micks go to celebrate their marriage?" I admitted I had never given that any thought at all but hoped they could pick up their plans soon.

Jack was a former smoker and had high blood pressure that was well-controlled with medication. At the time of admission, he hopped off the gurney and was pacing around the room. Radiology studies in the ED showed lung injury consistent with acute respiratory distress syndrome (ARDS). Nevertheless, he was up in his room, and despite having very low pulse ox readings, was conversational and tolerating his oxygen mask well. He was ready to "kick this COVID-19 in the ass and get the devil out of here." His pulse ox reading was 82, which is so low that a Code Blue would usually be called. The way Jack was acting versus his physical findings was disturbing. I was learning that this isn't uncommon in COVID-19 patients. Patients acted fine until their bodies could no longer compensate.

Jack used FaceTime with Kevin while we completed his history and physical assessment. Kevin was a studious-looking man with an open face and deep brown eyes. I could see why people felt they could trust him to sell or buy their houses. Both Jack and Kevin conferred about the timeline for Jack's symptoms. Kevin mentioned that while he was not showing houses during the quarantine, he did go into the office to check his mail every few days and often ran into other real estate agents who scoffed at the need for masks. A few days ago, Jack went with him to the office just to get out of the house. Kevin was convinced that Jack had caught COVID-19 from one of the agents.

I reminded Jack to take it easy and conserve his energy since COVID-19 could be sneaky. Symptoms could get worse suddenly. I wished Jack and Kevin well and left for the next proning assignment. What a delightful couple.

Our next patient was Eva Kranz, a 30-year-old woman who was 28 weeks pregnant and in severe respiratory distress from

COVID. Pregnant women are not typically cared for in a general adult unit, but the OB unit could not risk having the virus spread to other mothers and babies. Consequently, an OB nurse was assigned to care for Eva with oversight from the ICU staff.

To protect Eva, this was the nurse's only assignment. Because of her uterine size, Eva could not be placed fully on her belly. A modified side-lying position had been effective for the past three days in keeping Eva's pulse ox reading above 90. She was able to swallow clear fluids and talk without gasping. Her husband Grady stayed by her side through a sharing program on their home computer and a tablet that Grady brought to hospital security, who delivered it to the unit. Their three-year-old daughter Maggie joined the conversation from time to time. Eva's mom and dad and Grady's parents shared the daily care of Maggie while Grady worked from home. Together, the families formed a protective COVID social bubble.

Grady had met our team last night and seemed happy to see our smiling eyes. The goal of Eva's care was to avoid oxygen deprivation stress on her and the baby. The couple agreed that it would be best if intubation and ventilation could be avoided. This would be possible as long as the baby's condition stayed stable. At this point, the baby ("my brudder," Maggie told us) had a steady heart rate of 145. Eva had been placed on an external fetal monitor and there were no signs of labor.

Eva told us it hadn't been as hard to breathe today, and she and Grady felt encouraged. The OB and Intensivist physicians visited from the doorway twice each day. Very little was known about the effect of COVID-19 on fetuses and newborns. Eva's medical care charted new territory, and the doctors were cautiously optimistic.

On this visit, we would turn Eva to her left side. The baby's oxygenation was evaluated by his heart rate. If fetuses have poor oxygenation, their heart rate drops below 120. Maggie's brudder tolerated left side-lying and supine positions best. Eva said it was easier to breathe on her left side, and her pulse ox stayed at 95 and above.

Grady was tired. It was nearing midnight and Maggie had been awake since 5:00 am. He would go to bed—with the tablet plugged in and turned on—after we finished positioning Eva.

It took nearly an hour to get Maggie and the baby comfortable. We stayed an extra couple of minutes to be sure she could drink a little fruit smoothie while laying on her side. Waving goodbye to Grady and the nurse and patting Eva's arm, we left and began the PPE removal routine.

While washing my hands, I noticed the code cart and a physician outside Jack's room. We had another 30-minute interval until the next scheduled turn, so I walked down toward the activity. CPR was in full swing in the room. Jack had been intubated and was placed on a ventilator. He seemed to be coughing and fighting the ventilator. I noticed the nurse anesthetist listen to both lungs to verify the tube was in the correct position. Sedation was ordered and given by the RN. Jack's heart rate was 50 and falling despite oxygenation.

A nasogastric or n/g tube was successfully passed to his stomach and some green stomach contents were removed. An n/g tube empties the stomach. A flat stomach doesn't get in the way of diaphragmatic function and lung expansion. Vomiting is a risk of intubation, too. Vomiting can cause aspiration, which happens when acidic stomach contents enter the lungs. An empty stomach largely eliminates both concerns.

I wondered how soon Jack would be taken back to the high-level ICU. The code had been going on for 25 minutes, according to the clock on the wall.

"I'm a nurse on the prone team. What's been his response?" I asked the doctor when he glanced my way.

"No response to O2, no urine output, can't get his heart rate above 60," he said.

"Has anybody talked to his husband?" I asked.

"His husb…oh right, you know him better than I do. Can the prone nurse call his family?"

"Yes, thanks," said the person taking notes. "It's a guy. Check the record. This is going straight to friggin' hell. Be careful what you say."

I found Kevin's number and called. He answered on the first ring. "Oh my God, tell me, is he dead? What happened? He got so winded and then someone came in and shut off his phone. Was that you? Who is this?"

"Kevin, this is Kit, the nurse you met earlier today when Jack was admitted. Kevin, Jack has had a setback because of the virus. Could you go someplace and sit down? I want to tell you."

"Okay, hold on. Jack's sister is here keeping me company. I'm going to put her on speaker…okay? Listen, sweetie, it's the hospital, Jack's gotten worse. It's the nurse. Okay, go ahead, Cat."

"Hi, I'm Kit, the nurse, are you ready?" I said. I've found that another introduction or asking a benign question is a great warning shot before delivering bad news.

"Yes," Kevin said.

"I'm afraid I have some serious news. Jack had some trouble breathing and his heart rate went down. It came on suddenly, as you could tell, Kevin. The special code team of doctors and nurses is with him now. He has been given medicine to relax him so a tube could be placed in his trachea, which is the airway in his throat. We are helping him breathe with a ventilator machine. He is getting medication to increase his heart rate and keep his blood pressure up." I paused.

"What now? What can we do?" he asked.

"Right now, I want you to know that everything is being done to get Jack stable and move him to the highest-level intensive care unit where he can be closely monitored. Please stay with your phone, and either a physician or I will call you when we know more," I said. "If you are someone who prays, this may help you relax a little."

There was a hiccup. "Okay."

"I'm going to hang up now, Kevin. Please stay by your phone with Jack's sister and we will call you as soon as we can. Okay?"

"Yes, thanks, nurse."

I went back to the room where CPR was continuing. Without CPR, Jack's heart was in asystole.

"Jack's husband and sister are aware of what's going on. They'll wait for more information from us," I said to the code team.

"How long's it been? Forty-five minutes? Let's try cardiac epi," said a voice in the room.

Epinephrine is a powerful cardiac stimulant. Usually, it is inserted into an IV during a Code Blue to stimulate cardiac activity. As a last resort, the drug may be inserted directly into the heart.

"There are high pulmonary pressures," called out the nurse anesthetist who was monitoring Jack's response to the ventilator. "Dear God, this disease decimates the lungs before my very eyes."

The long needle and syringe containing epinephrine were handed to the physician. She inserted the needle, verified it was in the heart, and injected the drug.

We waited. There was no response.

"I'm sorry to say, we're going to call it," said the physician using the phrase that meant the resuscitation efforts were to be stopped. "Time of death, 12:56 a.m."

The Code Blue was over.

"Would you like me to get the family on the phone?" I asked the physician, whose name I still didn't know.

"Sure," she said.

I gave the physician a quick summary of names and relationships so that since she was calling with the worse possible news, she could convey an empathic tone. "You'll be talking to Kevin Finnegan, Jack's husband. Jack's name was Jack

O'Rourke. Jack's sister will be on the call, too. I don't know her name. They know his condition was very bad."

She nodded and I called Kevin. "Kevin, this is Kit again. Could you put your phone on speaker so Jack's sister can hear, too? Thanks. I'm going to turn the phone over to the doctor."

"Hello, Mr. Finnegan? My name is Dr. Tarrigan. I'm afraid I have some sad news to tell you."

I felt a hand on my shoulder and saw Jackie standing there. "Rob has agreed we can wait another half hour to turn the next patient. She's fast asleep and seems comfortable. Let's see if we can help in Jack's room."

Jack's assigned nurse was pleased to turn over the post-mortem care to Jackie and me. We bathed Jack, placed on him a clean hospital gown, and covered him to his neck. Usually, bodies are taken to the morgue in a special gurney with a false compartment where the mattress is. It allows bodies to be transferred while appearing as though the gurney was empty. Tonight, because of the number of deaths that occurred on this shift, there was not a special cart available. Consequently, when we finished, we escorted Jack's body to the morgue with his head uncovered. It was TSU Health System policy that no carts were to be transported with covered bodies. Covered bodies were understood by practically everyone as meaning "somebody died." Not to put too fine a point on it, but that's a negative message for hospitals to send.

Saying a silent prayer of thanks that it was the night shift, and all visitors were banned because of COVID-19, we made our way to the basement. A second unpleasant surprise was that there was no room in the morgue for Jack's body. There had been so many deaths that a refrigerated grocery store truck had been parked behind Building D. Jack's body needed to go there. A morgue attendant with a deep voice dressed from head to toe in PPE accompanied us. We rode back up to the main floor and out the employee entrance.

"Thank you," was all Jackie said when the attendant returned the cart to us. I was still too stunned to speak. My stomach felt like it had been punched. Not only had I seen firsthand how fast COVID-19 can kill, but I was hit with the realization that the death rate was higher than I had imagined.

We went to the alcove to wait for our team and report on the next patient.

"Oh, Kit," Jackie said. "Was that as awful for you?"

"This is so much worse. Refrigerated trucks…" I replied.

Wordlessly, a unit clerk walked by and handed us each a solid chocolate bunny.

That small act of kindness was all it took. I cried for the first time.

Chapter Twenty-Four

R-Squared: Repetitious Ruminations

*W*ork is weird. It's not that I'm intimidated by the big university hospital. I hate to break it to the nurses who think they're fancy pants for working there, but I'm not a backwater bumpkin. We don't have some of the amazing lifesaving technology at home. But we see enough, and we even have (gasp!) the same access to new knowledge and the same nursing theory-centered mission of care. OK. Self-righteous speech is now over.

It's not the hard work that's getting to me either. Hell (to borrow a Tala exclamation), I worked my behind off every day in Thompson. I like my whole prone team. We work well together, and the physical part of the job hasn't been that much more strenuous than I'm used to.

It's not even death. Death was not an infrequent visitor on 3 North at TMH. It wasn't even that people were dying with only strangers around them. I realized long ago that family support was not predictable, even when a person was dying. I held the hands of many dying patients who had outlived their friends and close family. Here's a little secret: we all die alone anyway. Being present helps the family, but the patient is quite literally, I believe, in another world at death.

What gets me is that almost half of my patients have died in the past three weeks. To have so little improvement for our *efforts is horrible. Nurses are supposed to heal or at least ease symptoms. It seems we're powerless.*

I'm lucky, really, if you can call it luck. I can have uninterrupted time turning patients. Even though the PPE gets in the way of offering the best emotional support, we're able to touch patients, give encouraging words, and let them know that they are the most important person to us during the time we're there.

It would be better to show my whole face to convey empathy, but nurses never stop looking for ways to reach out. So, get this... I've been playing around with makeup on my eyes and eyebrows. Not the kind of makeup that says, "Hey there, big boy!" but the kind that makes my eyes look more open and my eyebrows more expressive. We wear eye goggles or face shields (depending on availability) because we're so close to their faces, so it helps to have quality eyebrow pomade. It's the best I can do, but I think it works.

Some of the patients have been eager to talk. Many revealed parts of their lives that they were proud of or regretted. Thank goodness I learned in my first year as an RN that people don't want to be pumped up with false hope or even praised for their endurance. They want to know that you believe what they have to say has value. That their work and love have importance. There aren't any magic words. Just open, clear eyes and artfully arched brows can be plenty enough. At least I sure hope so.

Some of the patients are too exhausted or frightened to talk. I've found that touching their shoulders or hands and saying something like "I'm Kit, a nurse, and I'm right here," can help. Warmth does pass through the gloves we use, and most people who are awake try to reach for my hands.

I was saying that I'm lucky. Compared to the staff nurses, I am flat-out blessed. They have crazy assignments of 4 to 5 critically ill patients, and they never stop moving from room to room. Keeping every patient's needs straight while getting in and out of PPE and knowing that death is just around the corner has to be the most stress the majority of us nurses have ever been under. Our team helps the other nurses when we can. If we have a break in the turning schedule, we spread out and assist. When nurses know colleagues are willing to help, the horrible days are less horrible.

Even though we are very close to the patient's face while turning, none of my prone team have gotten sick. Two of the full-time nurses have contracted COVID-19. Both are still off-schedule, although they didn't have to be hospitalized. Their families had to be quarantined for two weeks and they have to stay in a separate part of the house until they have a negative test.

As far as I know, only minimal progress has been realized toward an effective treatment for COVID. That, however, is not stopping even anecdotal evidence from being seized upon as a cure. Some suggestions were truly ridiculous and sad in a frightening sort of way. My Gram says that those who came of age after World War II are simply accustomed to medicine being able to cure, treat, or prevent almost any disease. To have no answers in the 21st century is unthinkable to them.

I feel like moving all the time. I'm not sleeping a full 7 or 8 hours. I know it's anxiety. After work, I go home and shower and then walk outside for two miles. If Mary or Erin is off, they might come with me. Just looking at springtime around me seems to help. Life is hidden in the winter, but the trees are budding, and early spring tulips and daffodils are coming up. If I walk and pay attention to fresh air and new greenness, then usually, I can sleep.

When I wake up early, like I did today, I bake. I'm getting pretty good at kneading dough. Frustration is helping guide my punching and rolling. I heard Matt say to Mary the other day that maybe they should talk me into staying permanently. Haha! That's how good my cinnamon rolls are! Thank you, Linda Ackerman, baking teacher extraordinaire!

Chapter Twenty-Five

"I get by with a little help from my friends."
- The Beatles

Texting is so wonderful. I did it all the time in school and before COVID, but these days, I really appreciate how quickly I can talk to people without getting in my car or calling them. Whenever I want to talk, the phone is there. After the Sip and Stitch friends, Harrison and Gram are my go-to textees.

One evening when I didn't have to work, I found myself in text conversations with Harrison and Gram at the same time.

Me: Hey Gram. Miss you. I'm still in San Davers. Are you okay?

Gram: Hi, my Kit. I'm just fine. I'm remembering now why I stopped working in the nursing units when I turned 55. The pace is never-ending. I've even scrounged up my support pantyhose from the old days! I sent a text to Teddy thanking him for talking me into getting the really good athletic shoes at Christmas time.

Me: Shoes make all the difference. I wish I had full-length support hose. Some nights, the knee highs aren't enough!

Gram: How are you and the prone team?

Me: It's OK. I'm glad to be working and we work together well. It's crazy, Gram. So many of our patients are dying. I usually write about them in my Ruminations and then put the situations in a box on a shelf in the back of my mind. Can't remember who told me to do that. Maybe Harrison, the chaplain in Thompson. I thought I was over crying when a patient died, but one man's death last week sent me over the edge.

Gram: I'm glad you still use your journal. I don't feel too bad staying home when I'm not at work. I'm getting caught up with my e-reader selections.

Me: Aren't you the cool Gram with an e-reader! I keep hearing about nurses getting COVID. We've had two but they're getting better at home.

Gram: We've lost a nurse to COVID-19. She was OK at work one day, and then on a vent the next day. She got better and was extubated. They sent her to the step-down unit, and she continued to improve. Then two days later, she got worse again. She went back to ICU, and they pulled life support yesterday. What a sad time. Her name was Delores, but we called her Del. She was two classes behind me at school, so she was just 62.

Me: That's awful. How are you doing?

Gram: I'm OK. Del was a widow and worked just a few days every pay period. Travel money, she called it. When staffing got so short, she started working full-time. Her family is devastated. She was so active. There's no funeral yet. Maybe in the summer, the outside can open up for gatherings. Funerals are widely underappreciated. They help those of us who are left behind.

Me: I can't wrap my brain around all this death. I never considered that funerals weren't possible during quarantine. Families and friends need to get together to comfort each other in a traditional way. I'm sure the funeral group at church is having fits. Nobody to make fried chicken and jello salad for. Seriously, though it's scaring me a little. I mean a lot.

Gram: Since you and Tala have become good friends, I've noticed you can use humor to help defuse sad things. If we didn't laugh, we'd sob. You know, I'm a little scared, too. I know that at least one of our patients developed COVID-19 while we were treating him. Turns out, myocardial infarction was the least of his problems. COVID on top of a heart attack. Gad. He's in ICU but I haven't heard any more.

Me: You're wearing N95 masks, right? And gloves? Can you get gowns? Were you exposed?

Gram: We have masks and gloves. They're N95 masks and we air them out in paper bags every night, but I'm not confident that we're OK. I mean, our patients usually don't need us to move them around, so we only get close for the assessment. This virus is so contagious. Haven't washed my hands so much since I worked in the nursery while I was in nursing school! Oh, and no, he wasn't my patient, so I wasn't exposed.

Me: I took care of an OB patient the other day. She seemed to be improving but I don't know if she and the baby survived. The last I heard she was transferred to a lower level of care. So that's good.

Gram: It's hard not to want to continue contact with patients that get to you. How is your body handling the constant wearing of N95 masks?

Me: My face and hands are raw. Speaking of the nursery, Erin told me the other day to use butt diaper paste on the broken skin on my face. It gets so damp from my breath, and I look red and blotchy. My face hurts like a sunburn. Since I don't take off my mask much, I haven't had to worry about scaring people with the color of my face with the paste smeared on it. It works, sort of.

Gram: Butt diaper paste? That's hilarious. I'm sure Amazon carries it. Amazon Prime and I are new best friends.

Me: Glad to help.

Harrison: Hi Kit, how are you? Miss you.

Me: Hi Harrison. I'm talking with Gram. We're about finished.
Hold on. I need to get the Thompson scoop.
Harrison: K.
Gram: I'm going to let you go honey. I'm tired and want to go to
bed. Love talking to you.
Me: Love you so much. I'm glad you texted.
Harrison: Well, I love you, too, Kit. What's been going on?
Me: Oh, good grief, I meant that for Gram.
Harrison: (laughing and crying emoji)
Me: Love you so much, Gram. Get this. Harrison just popped
into my texts, and I sent this message to him instead of
to you. Now I have to explain why I professed my love
for him!
Gram: (the same laughing and crying emoji that Harrison sent)
Well, he seems like a nice man. Isn't he the chaplain? Don't
you work together at the church? Tell him you meant broth-
erly love, not hottie-totsy love.
Me: Yes and yes. You are so much fun. Yes, I'll tell him! Love
you. XXXXXX OOOOOO
Gram: 'Night to you and Harrison too. (another laughing emoji)
You made my night.
Me: I'm back Harrison. Listen, I meant to say I love you like you
know, brotherly love, not like you know, romantic love.
Harrison: Oh, darn it! And I was getting so hopeful! Well, I'll
take brotherly love for now. BTW was that a brotherly or
romantic kiss you gave me before you left for San Davers??
Me: OK. Here I am changing the subject. What's going on in
Thompson?
Harrison: Thompson is OK. We do have COVID here now and
the ICU is the COVID unit. The CCU is considered clean.
Critically ill coronary heart patients and those who have
had emergency surgery or trauma are going to CCU.
Me: I love how you use the same medical and lay terminology
in a sentence. Coronary heart patients. It's the same thing.

Harrison: I know but it helps patients when I do it and it's a hard habit to break.

Me: Just giving you a hard time, my brotherly friend. Listen, what do you hear about the furlough ending?

Harrison: They've called back some nurses, especially on 3 North because that's now the COVID-19 step-down unit. I'll bet you'll be back here pretty soon. When're the five weeks supposed to be up?

Me: The end of April. Are you seeing a lot of patients die?

Harrison: It seems 80% of what I do is go from room to room to give a blessing for the dying or prayers for overcoming the end stages of COVID. The rest of the time is calling in the priest, imam, or rabbi for the Roman Catholic, Muslim, and Jewish patients who ask. When I'm not doing that, I'm on FaceTime or some video platform talking to families after their loved one has died.

Me: That sounds so depressing.

Harrison: You know, a patient who is Muslim actually comforted me today. I asked him if I could call his imam for him for spiritual support. He said, "You know, we're all on the same journey. We climb the same steep, rocky mountain. I am happy to pray with you, chaplain." That struck me as so profound. It was like we really are all in this together.

Me: That's beautiful. He's right. We're all climbing the same steep, rocky mountain. I can't get over all the work we do to support people from COVID-19 only to have them die anyway. Those who are sick with other things like diabetes are so much worse off down here.

Harrison: And pray. God and I have been sparring the past few weeks. I get it that some of God's plans are mysterious. I get it that evil and death aren't God's fault. But really? You can't give us a break from this? What's the point? Why aren't you stopping this?

Me: I hear you.

Harrison: I'm sorry Kit, I just needed to talk. When I walked out of the hospital tonight and saw a Grocery Mart refrigerated truck at the side of the hospital, I almost lost it myself. Who's that swearing nurse? I needed her today.

Me: That's Tala and she could give you some outstanding swear words. I have to tell you that when I had to take a body to a refrigerated truck, it was surreal. I actually cried for the patient that day. It wasn't the death as much as what somebody did after I got back from that makeshift "morgue." A unit clerk handed me some candy and patted my shoulder. It was the kindness that did me in!

Harrison: You're so right. Oh, Kit. I'm glad we're talking tonight. I needed to be reminded that it's love that I should be thanking God for, not yelling at him for all this horrendous BS.

Me: A wise chaplain once told me that God has broad shoulders and can take it when we yell. BTW congratulations! You said BS! Way to go with the almost swearing!

Harrison: You must think I don't know anything about creative language. I'm not just a lamb in the woods, you know!

Me: Sorry, Mr. Bon Vivant. Didn't realize you were such a sophisticated citizen of the world.

Harrison: I like your quick comebacks. You've calmed me down, thank you. I'm getting sleepy now. Good night. Love you.

Me: You and Gram were just what I needed tonight too. 'Night.

Fifteen minutes later.

Me: Love you too, Harrison.

Chapter Twenty-Six

"The night is given to us to take breath, pray
and drink deep at the fountain of power."
- Florence Nightingale

Because I worked nights and my COVID social bubble people all worked days, I didn't see anyone at home for about five days. On the Tuesday before Easter, Matt, Mark, Mary, Erin, and I were all off. Mark offered to cook dinner. All we needed to do was come to Mark and Matt's place and bring two bottles of red wine.

I had missed seeing everyone together, and even though Mark could be the most pretentious health nut, he was growing on me. That meant I could stay in a room with him longer than 20 minutes without wanting to scream, "You are such a self-centered twit." Besides, I really liked the others.

While getting ready to leave, Mary said, "You know, we might want to have some of Kit's banana bread before we go. Mark's cooking, and we might just have seeds and nuts for dinner." Erin and I started to laugh, but then saw the wisdom in her remark. I cut three generous portions of bread and we ate them with orange cinnamon tea.

Thus, fortified and prepared for whatever Mark might be cooking up, we all got in my car and drove the five miles to one of the most gorgeous Victorian mansions that San Davers had to offer. San Davers started to become a prosperous community in the late 19th century. In those days, the very wealthy lived "in the suburbs." To get to these old-time suburbs, we took Main Street about five miles from downtown. Main Street turned into Main Boulevard, a wide tree-shaded street with stone center strips. This neighborhood, where the spectacular and very large old homes are located, was called the Gem District. Emerald Boulevard, Ruby Boulevard, and Sapphire Boulevard were connected by a small cobblestone paved street called Pearl Avenue. Ever since I was a little girl, when we would visit Gram, Dad drove us through the Gem District. My wish was to live in one of those manses.

As in most of my dreams, I arrived a little late to the heyday. The houses had largely been converted into apartments and duplexes. There was a District Association that governed the street view of houses so that the faces of each house were historically preserved. It remains a lovely drive today.

Matt and Mark lived in a two-story duplex on Sapphire. When the houses were built, no one had cars or garages. The buildings in the back were stables, and a common driveway was shared every two houses. Parking on a shared driveway could be a tricky business, especially if a neighbor wanted in or out. So, we parked on the street. Carrying our two bottles of Merlot, we walked up to the black front door with an etched glass front. The houses were so soundproof that I couldn't hear if the doorbell chimed inside. Seconds later, Matt opened the door with a flourish and invited us in.

"Mark is going berserk in the kitchen," he said after greeting us with fist bumps.

"Here's the wine," I said, hoping to avoid whatever Mark looked like when he was "berserk." Regular Mark had enough energy for a pack of poodles.

"Go ahead and take it in, Kit. He's concerned about the time it takes to breathe," he said with an eye roll.

I walked into the kitchen and saw Mark flitting around a center island loaded with food and multicolored bottles. I had to say that the kitchen was a bit of a shock following the Victorian vibe of the front of the house. The kitchen had been remodeled within the 21st century, which is to say it had oak cabinets, a microwave, gas stove, dishwasher, and polished nickel faucets. The counters were a gray solid surface. I'm not an interior designer, but it was a decently equipped little space.

"Oh, hi," said Mark looking genuinely glad to see me. "Could you uncork the bottles? Do both bottles. I want to make sure they have at least a half hour to breathe."

"I didn't know wine was so out of breath," I said.

Mark looked at me like I'd just said something painfully ignorant. "Oh, I see. That was a joke," he said. "I just want to be sure the tannins have time to soften."

Now, lest you think I'm a total wine dope, I want you to know that I understand tannins. After all, I took a three-class wine tasting course on my last vacation. From what I could recall (there were lots of wines to taste and I tried them all because I'm a good pupil, so my memory may not be precise), tannins were mostly found in red wine, and they come from the grape skins. When wine was left open to breathe, the tannins didn't taste as biting or astringent.

"Well, Mark, there you go," I said, popping the last cork.

"Great. I have Kir Royale for our aperitif," he said.

Whoa! This was serious dinner business! We'd "studied" Kir Royale in my wine class, too. It was served as a celebratory drink at the end of the course. I watched Mark mix one part crème de cassis with four parts champagne and my heart began singing. Those little glasses contained a magic potion.

"Can you help me carry out the glasses?" he asked. "I've got the almonds and olives."

I could learn to live like this, I thought. The black currant taste of the crème de cassis gave a happy kick to the champagne. Almonds and olives were a perfect accompaniment.

Then Mark had to break the mood by expounding.

"You know," said Mr. Nutrition-is-my-life-and-ought-to-be-yours-too-if-you-care-about-your-health, "black currants have a long history of treating disease. They contain iron and C and B vitamins. There is a proven effect on immunity."

I decided to cut Mark a break since this was the most delightful time I had had since…well, since COVID-19 had entered my world.

Mark's culinary skills were on full display that evening. We had white fish, some colorful vegetables roasted to perfection, brown rice, and…dark chocolates rolled in some seeds for dessert. Even Mark's ongoing chatter about the antioxidative properties found in each of the foods he served, and the disgrace of the Western diet went into my consciousness and darted out.

I did get some useful information that I planned to use the next time I choose a snack. Did you know that red wine and dark chocolate contain flavonoids that boost immunity? Yes! Cocoa and red wine contain Vitamin E and Vitamin C, which work in synergy to promote protective chemical reactions at the cellular level. Having a dark chocolate bar and a glass of red wine after work is not a sign of dysfunction; it was proof that I take immunity seriously! Chemistry could be fun.

I'm not sure if it was the healthy wine or the good food, but I started to feel kindlier toward Mark. He may have been a health bore, but he could cook.

"My Gram would love this," I said. "She's a nurse, too, and takes nutrition pretty seriously. Maybe you've met her on one of your runs to St. Luke's, Matt. She's returned to work in the CCU during COVID-19, but her official job is cardiac nursing quality improvement. Her name's Jennifer Wilson."

Mark started to cough. And cough.

"Are you okay? Have some water. Can you speak? Need a Heimlich?" we all said.

"I'm fine. Your Gram sounds interesting, Kit."

The rest of the evening was spent talking around the dining room table. Matt was a fabulous host, allowing the conversation to flow amicably and keeping Mark from monopolizing. Of course, the topic of work was paramount. We especially talked about the difficulties communicating through a mask and face shield. The issues led us to consider how to pantomime feelings and ideas. The conversation turned into a game of charades.

"Batman! No? Superman? No? *The Godfather*! Yes!"

"Running on a treadmill? Of course, you would choose something like that, Mark. Our patients are all too sick to be running on treadmills! It's the nurses who are running like that all day."

By the time we guessed the song "I Want a Hippopotamus for Christmas," it was 9 pm. Mary and Erin were working the next day and needed to get home to bed.

"You girls are such wimps," said the ever-charming Mark. "There's almost a full second bottle of wine left."

"You know, Mark, you have such a way of respectfully addressing us girls," I said. "Really. Girls? Who are you? A Baby Boomer in disguise? Just recork the wine and put it in a cool place. It'll be perfectly fine some other time."

Just as I was leaving, Mark tapped me on the shoulder. I turned and he gave me a tight hug. His face was turned away, of course. Because COVID. I was so shocked that I turned toward him.

"You're okay, Kit," he said, and then kissed my forehead and cheeks. "Sorry about the girls' remark. Sometimes I'm such an ass that I even shock myself. This was nice. Talk to you soon."

I'll be double-dipped. I did not see that coming. Those biceps gave a most satisfactory hug.

Chapter Twenty-Seven

"Our first journey is to find that special place for us."
- Florence Nightingale

On the Thursday before Easter, I received word that my furlough was ending. I was needed back in Thompson. Because COVID was spreading quickly throughout the state, our prone team was disbanded and we were dispersed back to our home hospitals. Jackie, Joan, Ken, Rob, and I were scheduled to work one last night at TSUH on Good Friday. My next shift would be on 3 North at 7 pm the day after Easter.

Our last night on 6 Southeast was uneventful. I must say that I was pleased that Kathy of the Band-Aid Station remark stopped my team after Shift Report. "I'm sorry if you thought I'd been insulting the first day you were here. You've worked out OK. Thanks for the help."

It wasn't a full-throated acknowledgment of our team's worth and since it seemed my duty was to take responsibility for her verbal slight, her words weren't a genuine apology either but, considering the source, I took it as a sincere compliment. At 7:30 am on Saturday morning, we told each other goodbye, made sure we had contact numbers, and set out separately to pack for home. Rob was a true role model, and I honestly told him that I hoped we met again under less pandemic circumstances. It was a productive three weeks. I was able to keep up with the rent and learned a whole lot about the early treatment of COVID.

Mary and Erin had to work and so we said goodbye last night. I planned to take a short nap and leave for Thompson around 1:00 pm.

Tala had to work tonight at the convent extended care center because the sisters were taking turns at an all-night Easter vigil and asked her to stay until Easter morning. We would see each other Monday evening at work.

On my way out of town, I repeated my route by driving by Gram's house. She was off work that day and came out to the sidewalk. "Bye, my Kit. It was nice to know you were in town. Stay safe at work, OK?"

"You too, Gram. Wish I could hug you."

"Me too. It'll be soon. I'm encouraged by the research so far."

Gram seemed to have connections all over the place, so I didn't bother asking her to explain what she meant. If Gram was encouraged, then I would follow her lead.

I stopped at the Food Mart on the way home. Here was another thing I could get used to. To keep customers safe, the store was using its online system. Groceries were ordered and paid for online. Then, at a time of their choosing, customers would drive to the parking lot and a masked person put their groceries in the car. It usually cost $5 for this service, but our store was waiving the fee during the COVID surge. No more wandering the aisles wondering where they put the items on my list each week. I was now a grocery store lady of leisure.

I reached my beautiful apartment by 4 pm. After putting the groceries away, I took a shower, and Netflix was streaming by 5 pm.

Dorothy was right. There's no place like home.

Chapter Twenty-Eight

"I am of certain convinced that the greatest heroes are those who do their duty in the daily grind of domestic affairs whilst the rest of the world whirls as a maddening dreidel."
- Florence Nightingale

On Easter Sunday, there was nothing to do. No church services. No Easter dinner at Mom and Dad's, although we decided to use Zoom to catch up at noon. Gram and I were virtual. Teddy, Kai, Mom and Dad, Amanda, and Maddy were at Mom and Dad's since they were their own COVID-safe bubble.

I decided to start the day by sending a text to Linda and Mark Ackerman, letting them know I was home.

Linda responded by putting eight freshly baked and still warm cinnamon rolls at my door. She knocked and ran back to her door. I put on my mask, and we waved at each other from across the hall.

"You're the best," I called.

"You don't need a mask this far away, Kit. Mark has the news on all the time, and it turns out masks aren't as good as some of the so-called experts say they are," said Linda.

"Wow. I haven't heard that about masks. It takes distance and masks to be really effective, that's for sure. Masks can help you protect other people, too. I'm going to wear mine." I said.

I heard Mark in the background say, "I'm not going to suffocate wearing a mask if it doesn't help me. The science is all wrong and the scientists are old and out of touch."

"Wow," I repeated, "I hadn't heard that either."

Linda's eyebrows arched and she frowned at me. "He's just impossible with that TV and his lodge buddies. I don't know what's true. I wear my Maddy mask when I go out and hope for the best."

Then, with a quick subject pivot, I smelled the freshly baked rolls and said, "You're like the Easter bunny by bringing cinnamon rolls. Thank you!"

We closed our doors and I leaned against mine. Who said masks weren't needed? What's a Maddy mask? Maybe I've been living under a rock. My only contacts for the last three weeks have been healthcare people and patients who had COVID. And Healthy Mark, who hardly counted, unless you believe that lifting weights or Zinc supplements will prevent COVID. But even he wore a mask when out with other people.

I hadn't talked face to face with my family since I left for San Davers. Texts and emails had to suffice. As far as I knew, everything was fine. During the past three weeks, I felt lucky just to keep up with news headlines, which seemed to be all COVID-related. Maybe I'd get the scoop on COVID in Thompson according to the Wilsons before going to work tomorrow night. If my conversation with Linda and Mark had been any indication, I had a lot to learn about what was going on outside hospital walls.

I walked six steps into my efficient galley kitchen and cut two cinnamon rolls for my Easter lunch. At noon on the dot, I clicked on the link, and my family opened up. Mandy, Maddy, Kai, Teddy, and Mom and Dad were all on one side of the dining room table. They pushed and pulled the laptop when they wanted to talk. Just listening to them made me happy. The longer the conversation went on, the more I was reminded of news headlines.

Mandy and Maddy officially became engaged last night! Hurray! They had no wedding plans, of course, until businesses start opening up again. Living arrangements were going to change, too. Tala, who shared Mandy's apartment, would be working in the hospital where she had a higher risk of COVID exposure. Her job would place Mandy at risk and would also mean that Mandy couldn't use the Wilson clan as her protective COVID bubble. So, since the engagement, it was decided Mandy will be moving into my old bedroom, setting up her home office at my old desk. She's a nurse consultant with a pharmaceutical company and could work from any location with Wi-Fi. As Tala was coming home tonight from the convent, Mandy was moving her stuff out this afternoon.

"I got a video from Susan Anderson yesterday on Instagram," said Mandy. "She sent a picture of herself, and a couple of other nurses all gowned, masked, shielded, and gloved. I couldn't tell for sure, but her eyes looked puffy. I texted her after I got the video, and she said 3 North nurses are working 40-48 hours every week like you said you were doing at Trail State. Plus, her fifth-grade son is going to school online, which hasn't been easy either. Doesn't sound like she's getting a lot of rest. The night staff is thrilled you're coming back tomorrow night. She said that work has been 'crazier than I've ever seen it.' I'll bet you've seen worse in San Davers, Kit, but it's getting intense here. Susan said that no matter what they do, almost half the COVID patients are dying. She sounded flapped, and Susan doesn't get easily flapped. Her text said a lot."

"I lost an old friend to the virus," said Gram. "She was a nurse and most likely contracted it from a patient or other staff member at work. It's been chaotic down here. I have respect for respiratory viruses. I can stay home when I'm not at the hospital and occupy myself all by myself just fine."

"We watch church from the couch on Sunday mornings since the quarantine started," said Mom.

"Communion is Ritz crackers and grape juice from our cupboard," said Maddy.

"I can wear my PJs to church," said Kai.

"Pastor Linda sends prayers," said Dad.

"My church is doing online services too. It's not the same, especially on Easter," said Gram. "COVID has put God on the hot seat. How can a loving God let this happen? Just this last week, I noticed that people on my Facebook page are saying that they don't trust medical experts and that the health organizations are telling us lies about COVID," Gram went on. "That's what they're calling it: lies. I asked one friend if she meant that we all had more to learn about this new virus, and she was adamant— no, it's lies. They want us all to think this is a big deal, but it's deception and a conspiracy to ruin the economy."

"Oh my gosh!" I said. "That sounds just like a conversation I had with my neighbors this morning, except for the economy part. I know that I can't figure out what to make of the spread of COVID and how fast it kills. If a nurse is confused about it, imagine what the general public thinks. It never occurred to me to think the pandemic was an economic-political plot."

"Hey, sis," Maddy chimed in. "You're probably just naïve about this because you're a nurse. Listen, what's causing all the job losses is this quarantine. They forced businesses to close and now no one is being paid. It's not your fault that you don't understand. It's complicated and hard to believe that you're being tricked."

Huh? Not my fault for what? Oh, buddy boy, you better watch it with your condescension. "Maddy, I just know that I saw a lot of people die from COVID-19 the last three weeks."

"That's what they want," Maddy went on. "They want you to be afraid, so you won't notice what their real agenda is. Those deaths are from sick old people who would have died anyway."

"I don't even know what you mean by that, Maddy. When I was in San Davers, it seemed like people were more afraid of dying from COVID-19 than anything else. You know, Harrison has always said that the biggest threat in a situation where you might die is the unknown. If you can't see something or if you can't predict what will happen, getting angry is a natural response to being frightened. It seems to me that when the unknown has a higher probability of killing you, getting mad seems like a sane reaction. Or at least understandable until you know more and can overcome the fear."

"Oh, honey," said a still star-eyed Mandy. "Kit's right. Fear of not knowing enough about COVID is causing a lot of this talk and making up possible reasons. Nobody is purposely lying to you."

"Maddy, the fact is that this virus is causing disease. The rest sounds mostly political," said Teddy.

"Yeah, whatever," said Maddy.

"Now, now," said Mom. "This isn't going to solve anything. Let's talk about something more cheerful. Are you seeing Harrison, Kit?"

I learned long ago that telling my family anything personal would result in a swarm of interest and oversight. I wasn't sure what Harrison and I were at that moment, but I was not going to give up any details. "Well, we work together at the hospital and at the Young Adults group," I said. "But we aren't dating."

"That's too bad, he seems nice."

"Oh, he is nice, but I'm not dating him. Speaking of church, do you know anything about the church's food bank? Since I'm back home, I'd better check with Pastor Linda to see if the Young Adults group is doing anything more with the food bank since people can't come in to get donations."

"How kind of you to think of that, Kit," said Dad. "I'm glad you're home."

Suddenly, Maddy and Mandy appeared on screen, wearing brightly colored masks. "Look what my wonderful Maddy is doing, Kit," said Mandy.

"I don't know anyone called 'Wonderful Maddy,'" I joked. "What's with the masks?"

It turns out that Maddy can sew! The "Googles" taught him a pattern and he was churning out masks for the neighbors and nurses at the hospital. They were double-layered and washable. There was even a little pouch between the layers. He said the pouch could hold folded tissue to increase barrier protection, and the tissue should be discarded frequently. Maybe Maddy wasn't as anti-COVID precautions as he was making it sound.

Maddy started making masks when Pastor Linda announced that the church recently received a large quantity of cotton blend fabric. It came from the estate of a member who had recently died. It was Old Mr. Kevin Grasser, my drama teacher! (God rest his soul. Even in death he's helping the town.) Apparently, O.M.K.G. made costumes for the community theater and had a stockpile of fabric when he died. I had heard he had cancer that had metastasized throughout his body. People were dying of things other than COVID-19. Maddy was right about that.

"There were ten garbage bags full of fabric. The quilting group took most of it. They let me have two bags in exchange for a dozen masks. I managed to get a bunch of elastic for the ear hooks online before the stock ran out."

"Now, he has something to do while everybody is working online," said Mandy. "He's been taking packs of masks over to TMH and they've happily taken each one. It's an extra layer of protection for the nurses who are reusing their N95s."

"I've seen some on family members when they come up to the drive-through for prescriptions," said Dad.

My opinion of Maddy went up a few notches. What a great way to stay busy and be useful.

"You're famous, Wonderful Maddy," I said. My neighbor got one of your masks and she calls it her Maddy Mask!"

"Hey, do I detect an entrepreneurial idea?" asked ever-ready-to-make-a-buck Teddy.

"Could you drop some by my apartment?" I asked. "The front desk has a slot to put envelopes and small packages. Put them in there. The manager will put it in my mailbox."

"For you, anything," Maddy said, and sat back, looking proud.

"You know, you guys," said Mandy, "a vaccine isn't too far away. My company's researchers are working on one with some other immunologists. Once we have a vaccine, everyone will be able to get protected and this will go away."

"From your lips to God's ears," said Dad.

"I miss you guys," I said. "What's going on at work and school? All school is online, right?"

"Finally! Does anybody want to hear about me?" asked Kai. "Does anybody even care about the Thompson High seniors? There's no prom, no graduation ceremony. We won't have senior skip day or anything that's important. You know our senior trip? We were supposed to take a trip to Broadway and the Guggenheim Museum. Nope. All closed down. Now, what do I have to look forward to? Nothing. Senior year fun is completely taken away."

"It's really been hard for Kai and his friends," said Dad. "Kai went with me to deliver prescriptions to patients who can't use the drive-through. Afterward, we drove by some of Kai's friends' houses. I took a box of candy from the store, and we put chocolate bars on everyone's porch. Kai arranged that by text."

"Yep, that's the biggest fun around here for a month," said Kai. "I'm being swindled out of the best year of high school!"

"That actually does sound awful," I said, remembering how dramatic I was as an 18-year-old. "Maybe by next month, things will get less intense."

"Yeah, maybe. Colleges are even shut down. Am I supposed to go to college in my bedroom on my laptop? What a rook."

"I'll keep my ears open at work for any ideas for you and your friends," I said. I was pretty sure that there was nothing a nurse at TMH could do about prom or graduation, but I felt like I should throw Kai a bone to give him some hope.

The look I got in return told me that he wasn't buying it. If I could put words to that look, it would be like, "Didn't you hear anything I just said? Things are horrible and nothing can be done!" Kai was right, I had to admit. I never went through anything like this in high school.

I was saved from further Kai-disdain by Teddy and Mom. They were ready to talk about school. Yes, they were teaching 100 percent online.

Teddy was OK with it. "It's a challenge, but this will be the wave of the future and I'm learning a lot." He was such an optimist, which was probably why he'd thrived as a public-school teacher for almost 8 years. High school was hard enough to teach face to face as a teacher, but at least Teddy's students would be able to get online themselves for class.

Ability and desire were two completely different things though. There was always the stipulation that his students will get online "if they felt like it." But Teddy taught advanced algebra and calculus, and these kids were not your usual school-skippers. Mom said that's why he's not so stressed.

Mom was having an especially hard time teaching online. "I'm trying all kinds of ways to get my third graders to stay interested in learning. I've even resorted to online games," she laughed. "Kai is teaching me how to play them. Last week, I adapted a game for a reading exercise. The kids stayed on and even participated. That one 45-minute period is the best it's been for a month."

"Mom's seriously thinking of retiring at the end of the year," said Dad. "I support her decision if that's what she chooses to do."

Mom has worked for Thompson Schools for 30 years, with three years off to have Teddy, Maddy, Kai, and me. She could retire this year but not with full benefits. To have the full benefits, she had to stay until she had 35 years of seniority.

"I'm not sure what to do," she said, sounding like she was going to cry. "I don't know how much more of this I can take.

The kids don't come online every day, or they don't come back after lunch and the parents are stressed because they're working from home plus trying to stay on top of their kid's schoolwork. I don't blame them for taking out some of their frustration by getting mad at the teacher, but I don't think I can stand being called 'lazy' or 'uncaring' much more often. If one more parent tells me that I've got it lucky to be off all summer and get paid for doing nothing, I'll…I'll…they don't pay me enough to put up with this."

"Oh, mom," I said. "I'm sorry. I'll listen to you whenever you want to talk."

"Thanks, honey," Mom sniffed.

"You're right," I said, giving my best Easter smile. "Let's talk about something we all love…eating at your house! What are you guys doing about Easter dinner today? I have some—"

"Yes, well, we better hang up now," said Mom. "We'll talk soon, Kit and Jen. Buckets and buckets of love to both of you! Happy Easter!"

"Bye then," I said to the blank screen.

Chapter Twenty-Nine

"Life is a hard fight, a struggle, a wrestling with
the principle of evil, hand to hand, foot to foot."
- Florence Nightingale

After the fam Zoom call, I had a hard time relaxing. Faced with the prospect of eating all the cinnamon rolls or using my nervous energy for good, I decided to compromise. I had another cinnamon roll and put on my walking shoes, yoga leggings, and a lined jacket.

Walking really helped me when I got caught up in my own mind. Maybe it was because I was such an introvert, but even though I was in a new environment, being quarantined didn't seem too bad while I was in San Davers. Except for work and my social bubble, I didn't feel as though I was missing out on anything. For sure, I was not very sensitive to how COVID-19 had been affecting those I love most.

There were a couple of patients in San Davers who got to me. I still think of the pregnant woman with COVID and wonder how she and the baby did. For the most part, I've been able to keep my work life separate from my personal life. I've been able to use the cheesecloth method I learned from my Sip and Stitch friends when I was a new grad.

The CHEESECLOTH TECHNIQUE (I think of it in caps) lets through my feelings of empathy and compassion, but not obsessive feelings about what I can do to fix my patients' problems. For a while, I had convinced myself that I and I alone was the answer to caring for my patients. That was not only patently ridiculous, but it was tearing me apart emotionally.

These days, the "box on the shelf" method was working. I grieved for a while, allowing the cheesecloth to do its job, put the situation on a back-of-the-mind-shelf, and then moved on to the next patient problem. There is always a next patient problem. I still enjoy nursing, so it's effective for now.

The prone team gave me good experience, but even though I worked hard, the stress wasn't the same as the nurses who had responsibility for multiple ICU patients in 12 hours. Wearing PPE all the time was truly tiring on top of constant monitoring, which required total focus that was exhausting. It was hard to explain how almost literally no downtime at work affected a nurse's health.

I did worry that I might not be prepared enough for the stress of a full shift in PPE. Working with good colleagues can make or break coping. I'd be glad to have Tela and Jacob on night shift with me.

Some of Maddy's comments today about unemployment got me thinking. My financial advisor, also known as my brother Teddy, taught me that the stock market was going gangbusters. He's been singing the praises of my investments since I started working in the "real" world. Today, however, I was reminded that maybe economic things weren't so rosy.

Teddy said that the economic expansion has been going on for ten years, and there's no reason to expect it will stop. Teddy also said whatever comes up has to come down. Within the last two months, especially since around St. Patrick's Day, people were out of work and businesses were shutting down. I was furloughed and would have been off for three weeks without pay if I hadn't gone to San Davers (note to self: call Teddy and ask him if my money was OK). I guess my job was safe now, and I was grateful for that. Teddy and Mom were working from home, despite how hard it was, but they were getting their paychecks.

I remembered that while growing up, around spring, Mom usually said that her class was driving her nuts. However, I never remembered her threatening to quit. I remembered kitchen calendars with countdowns to the next teacher and student break, but I'd never heard her talk like she did today.

Mandy's job hadn't changed much since she almost always worked from home. Maddy said his unemployment had been approved. Since he lived at home, I wasn't concerned he would be turned out on the streets or not have food.

I needed to get back to TMH and see what was going on.

Chapter Thirty

**"The very first requirement in a hospital is
that it should do the sick no harm."**
- Florence Nightingale

I decided to arrive at work 30 minutes early on the first night back, and I was glad I did. It felt good to drive the familiar route and park in the employee lot.

Putting on a Maddy mask, I got out of my car. Walking in, I noticed the visitor lot had a number of cars with people sitting in them, staring at the hospital, or using their phones. I was accustomed to seeing this in San Davers. No one who was not a hospital employee was allowed in the hospital building.

Families who had loved ones critically ill with COVID often took turns waiting in the parking lot. Most people told the ICU nurses that it helped them to feel closer and more supportive than waiting at home. I noticed that some families had erected posters on their cars that said, "Love You, Dad" and "We're Here for You, Mom." An especially poignant one read, "Happy 43rd Anniversary, My Darling Lily!"

The lobby was deserted except for a security guard. Usually, the lobby has a quiet undertone of voices and shoe noise. The guard looked bored out of his mind but sat up straighter at his desk when I entered.

I felt comfortable in hospitals. Hospital lobbies seem to smell the same everywhere. From the first day I arrived at TMH as a new graduate, I thought of the lobby odor as almost having a hue:

summer-sky blue. The air seemed as clear, filtered, and clean as the sky after a Midwest June rain. It may have been a nurse thing to feel the hospital atmosphere in my eyes and nose and mind, but for whatever reason, the ambiance was familiar and comforting. Taking a deep breath, I switched my mind to work mode.

My unit 3 North has been converted to a step-down COVID-19 unit. Other adult patients who didn't have COVID-19 were being admitted to 3 South. Tonight, I was assigned to 3 North. The unit I was assigned to depended on the staffing needs. When I was a new graduate, there were two semi-private rooms on 3 North. Now, every room was private, and there were 38 beds. Each wing had 14 beds, and the center hall had ten beds.

I noticed day-shift nurses had their photos on the front of their scrubs, so I was glad I wore mine. I was greeted by Barb, the dayshift charge nurse and my former mentor. She was thrilled to see me.

"C'mon, Kit," she said. "Let's get you your N95. There're some staffing things you need to know about, too."

We started at the MED dispenser where I learned N95 masks were counted every shift. "Why the big deal about counting masks?" I asked.

"You're going to love this," said Barb as she vigorously opened the MED door. "Dr. Weaver is worried that we will use the masks indiscriminately. Since they're in short supply, we have to count them every shift and compare the numbers of masks used with the number of masks returned."

Like we were going to protect ourselves too much? I could see it now on Amazon Prime: *Kit Wilson, RN: Black Market Mask Supplier! Buy your N95 masks here. Free shipping.* What were we to do if our mask broke, got wet, or was contaminated some other way?

As if reading my mind, Barb said, "You can get another mask if yours is clearly contaminated. You have to sign out a new one and save your old one for administration to check."

Seriously? So, who had been reassigned to make sure nurses weren't going around recklessly using respiratory protective gear during a respiratory pandemic? Was this a nursing administrator or some guy from finance? Probably from finance. The guys holding the purse strings seemed to believe nurses couldn't figure out the differences between inadequate supply, legitimate protection, or simply wasting hospital resources.

I mean, really. What if the administrator thought the mask wasn't bad enough to exchange? Did we get a demerit or have the cost of a mask taken out of our paycheck? Wait until Tela got wind of this latest attempt to monitor nurses' behavior, I thought. I could already hear her: "The hell you say!"

"Here's your N95 and your paper bag to store it in between shifts. The window counter near the main unit doors is the place where all the bags are supposed to be placed.

"Deb Hillman was supposed to be in charge tonight. She called off with a fever and sore throat," continued Barb. "Sounds like COVID. She'll get a test tomorrow, I guess. Another nurse bites the dust. COVID has us down two nurses now. One on days, and one on nights."

"Who is on tonight?" I asked.

"You, Tala, and Jacob right now. Connor is your certified nursing assistant. There's a unit clerk scheduled for both 3 North and 3 South, so you'll have some help with orders."

"Three RNs for 38 COVID patients who are all on oxygen, cardiac telemetry monitors, and multiple IVs? How many have to be proned during the shift?" I said in a very low are-you-freaking-kidding-me voice.

Oh, God help us. I felt cold all over.

"Patrick is on call tonight. I got approval for him to work the full shift even though it's overtime. It will be his fourth 12-hour shift in the past six days." said Barb. "I'm really sorry. Staffing is down to the bone. Nights are only scheduling four

RNs, and most nights the on-call person works their additional four hours."

"You can close your mouth, Kit," said the day-unit clerk. "It is what it is."

I felt another presence beside me. "What the hell does that even mean?" said Tala. "We've got a 10:1 patient-to-nurse ratio. That's two RNs short. So, it's just the way things are and too bad for you? It is what it is. What a lame expression."

"Let's take this conversation out of the hallway," said Barb. "I can fill you in during Report."

Jacob, Tala, and I went into the conference room for Report. The whole idea of the Walking Report was on hold. Patrick came in just as I was closing the door.

"Thank you for agreeing to work the whole shift, my friend," I said.

The four of us went into our let's-figure-out-this-crisis method of patient care. This was definitely an RN thing. Although we could complain with the best of them, we were masters at solving the problem right in front of us. We knew we could voice our concerns about staffing and figure out a long-term solution later. Right now, the priority was patient safety.

Jacob agreed to do charge duties. He directed Connor, our CNA, to do a quick walk through the unit and see if any patient was in immediate need of an RN. Next, we decided to split the unit into two patient teams. Tala and I took 20 patients. Jacob and Patrick took 18 patients because Jacob had charge nurse responsibilities beyond patient care.

In the conference room, we arranged ourselves at least six feet apart, wearing our masks. Barb started Report. Every patient was on oxygen. Because the ICU was full of intubated patients on ventilators, even patients with high-flow oxygen masks were out of ICU and on 3 North. Every patient was on cardiac telemetry.

"The night unit clerk's assignment is split between 3 North and 3 South. When she is able to be on 3 North, Emily told me she knew how to respond to cardiac alarms," Barb said, referring to Emily Smith, our 3 North nursing manager. "This clerk's not one of our regulars. I don't know her. When she's not here, keep alarms at the highest volume possible. I don't know if you know this, Tela and Kit, but all 3 North rooms are negative pressure now. Some rooms were converted, and most have negative venting fans in the rooms. The fans are loud, although some patients have said they have gotten used to it, like white noise. Remember, doors have to be closed to sustain negative air pressure and vent air outside."

Although none of us said this out loud, we each knew this was a serious safety concern because we wouldn't be able to hear alarms very well with doors closed and loud fans running. There were yellow and red cardiac alarm lights outside each room, but if you were in someone else's room and not in the hallway, there would be no way to know an alarm was sounding. We would need to watch one another's backsides all shift.

If possible, we were to turn 10 of the patients from supine to prone or prone to supine. The night supervisor could be paged to help turn patients if she was free, and Respiratory Therapy could be paged to see if there was a therapist available. Since it took at least five people and 30 minutes to turn a patient, I was having a hard time adding up enough staff to prone 10 patients and also care for the 28 others.

There were about a dozen patients who had requested to not be intubated under any circumstances. If they "crashed" or became seriously ill and oxygen wasn't helping, we were only to do supportive care. They had a designation of "DNR," or "Do Not Resuscitate." Barb told us she checked this afternoon and all the patients with that designation had a signed consent uploaded in TIMES.

One patient died on 3 North on the day shift. He was an elderly gentleman in his late 70s with multiple chronic illnesses before he'd developed COVID-related pneumonia.

"I was with him when he died," Barb said with tear-filled eyes. "He said 'Something's gonna get me, might as well be this stuff.' Chaplain Harrison was with him about 30 minutes before he crashed."

As Report went on, I was struck by the sameness of every-one's care. At this stage of the pandemic, care was mainly sup-portive: oxygen, positioning, IV fluids, oral fluids, food as tol-erated, and proning as tolerated. There was no treatment that conclusively worked.

As Barb was leaving, a diminutive woman knocked and entered the room.

"Hi. I'm Bree. I'm assigned as a unit clerk on 3 North and 3 South tonight. I usually work in Cardiac Procedures as a CNA and do unit clerk stuff down there too. There aren't any cardiac procedures scheduled for a while, so I'm floating around the hospital.

"Listen, 3 South doesn't have anything for me right now. I can read monitors and it sounds like you need more help than they do because of your cardiac monitors and not enough nurses, so I told them I was going to stay here with you all night and they should call me if they need something right away." She paused and took a breath. "I just wanted you to know I'm here, okay? I'm usually on day shift, so I need to stay busy. I'm awake, so don't worry, I won't go to sleep on you."

We stared at her for just a moment. Her soliloquy was unex-pected and seemed to surprise us all.

"Well, my newest and dearest pal," said Tala. "I'm sorry we can't hug you. Thank you!"

"Yes," said Jacob. "We can use you more than we can say."

"Okay, good," said Bree. "I paged the night supervisor and told her my plan. She told me to do whatever works with the charge nurses and she'd come up here later. Okay?"

"Oh my gosh, that is definitely okay," Patrick said.

"Better than okay," I chimed in.

"It's 7:35 pm," said Jacob. "Let's get this show on the road."

I honestly don't remember much about that night. By the time Tala and I had made rounds and passed medications to our ten patients each, it was 10:30 pm. At that time, we decided to see if anyone was able to help us reposition our five patients who were due to be placed from prone to supine.

I was documenting the initial assessment on TIMES when Bree told me that the supervisor was tied up and couldn't come help for "a while." The respiratory therapist was involved in a Code Blue in ICU. Repositioning would have to wait until we had enough staff to perform the procedure safely.

I said, "Let's go around again to each room together and see what's what. It's been over two hours since I've seen some of the patients."

"Yep," Tala agreed. "Race you to the PPE on the door!"

We had to wear PPE to enter each room. I'd become proficient at that in San Davers, and I could safely don and doff PPE in a few moments. Tala kept up with me.

Bree paged Tala about an hour later when we were with our sixth patient.

"Bradycardia of 50 and pulse ox 87," said Bree. "Room 312. Patient Heidi Brandt."

"You go," I said. "I'll finish here and catch up. Page me if you need another nurse."

Tala was out of the room and at the handwashing sink in less than one minute. I finished rounds at 0200 hours (2 am). The supervisor and respiratory therapist appeared, and with Patrick, helped us turn two of my assigned patients and two of Patrick's. I still had not seen Tala. It was 0430 (4:30 am).

I leaned against a wall and closed my eyes. I would have been able to sleep in that position but for the sudden and severe leg cramps in my right calf. It almost took me to the floor. Like a mind reader, Bree appeared with a gigantic bottle of electrolyte water.

"Your cramps are from dehydration, no rest, and some sodium depletion," she said. "Drink this. You haven't stopped all night."

I was thirsty and drank the salty-tasting liquid in three long swallows. I hobbled to the restroom (another neglected task in the last 10 hours) and was a new woman within 15 minutes.

"I'll replace your sports drink," I called to Bree as I passed the central station. "It really worked."

"Glad it helped. Dietary is now stocking it in the staff refrigerator."

"Where's Tala?" I asked.

"She's been in and out of room 312 since about 2 am. The lady has a DNR status. The chaplain just went in."

I made quick rounds one more time and went to room 312 just as Harrison and Tala came out. Tala shook her head. "I was able to give her something in the IV for her breathless feelings and cranked up the oxygen. That's all I could do except be there. She passed just a few moments ago. I'm on my way to call the family."

"It's good to see you Kit," said Harrison. "I've missed you."

"What in the world are you doing here at 5:00 in the morning?" I asked him. "You left about nine hours ago."

"Well, I'm glad you're happy to see me," Harrison said, his eyes crinkling. "One of our chaplains and the Catholic priest both have COVID, so I volunteered to work longer hours each day. A deacon is covering the priest as much as he can. I'm able to get seven or eight hours of rest every day, so it's all good."

"I am happy to see you, but I had no idea until tonight how short-staffed we were," I said. "This is more than a tiny bit scary."

"Yes, it is," he agreed, shaking his head. "You'll be asked to work extra. It's okay to say no, but you'll be asked in pitiful begging tones."

"You are such a kind shepherd," I said, referring to the role of the clergy as a spiritual guide and comforter.

"Hey Kit, I know you have to go, but one quick thing. Would you be in my social bubble?"

The way Harrison phrased the invitation sounded both provocative and welcoming. We looked at each other and started to laugh.

"Well, Harrison, I've never been propositioned like that before. But yes, it will be my pleasure to be in your social bubble," I said with a wink. "I have to run now, though."

He turned and walked away with a backward wave. "Really glad you're back, Kit."

I met up with Jacob for a couple of minutes. Patrick had a patient die tonight, too, and Connor was helping him. Since Bree was also a CNA, she was helping Tala with Heidi Brandt's post-mortem care.

I stayed on autopilot until 8 am. I gave Report to day shift, finished up TIMES documentation, and checked the MED records again to be sure all medications were documented, and none were missed.

Tala, Patrick, and I put our masks in paper bags on the windowsill and silently left together.

"I'm glad we had Bree," said Tala. Patrick and I nodded.

"Are you on tonight?" I asked. Tala and Patrick nodded.

I drove home with the windows down and the '90s oldies on my radio. There were strawberry scones next to my apartment door with a note. *Thinking of you. XX00 Linda.* I ate one scone while undressing for my shower, and another while blow-drying my hair.

Crawling into bed, I whispered, "Thank you God for getting me through this awful night. Please protect my patients from anything I wasn't able to do for them."

Sleep descended like a veil.

Chapter Thirty-One

"**Professional nurses have a duty to care
during crises like pandemics.**"
- American Nurses Association 2020

The first six weeks I was back in Thompson went by in a blur. I worked three 12-hour shifts a week and usually one or two additional six-hour shifts. The overtime pay was good, but I was exhausted. Tala, Jacob, and I stayed together on the same 12-hour shift schedule. We split our time off to help cover short staffing.

The census remained high, which was not in itself a particularly strange occurrence. 3 North was usually full or with one or two empty beds. It wasn't the number of patients that got to me; it was what I'd come to call COVID-19's Mind-blowing Context or MBC. That means the census and the patient care needs and unique demands placed on caregivers had to all be considered together to fully understand the situation we nurses found ourselves in. There were no words strong enough to describe MBC.

First, there was PPE. Secondly, there was short staffing caused by nurses falling ill with COVID or simply quitting. Finally, was the acuity or sickness level of the people we cared for with COVID-19.

As for the PPE, to care for each patient, nurses needed to wear a large amount of personal protective equipment. Putting on and taking off gowns, gloves, masks, face shields, and performing the prescribed hand hygiene process took time. It could be done in about two to three minutes, but that ended up being four to six minutes per patient visit with every patient, every time. Just to give an idea, if I was in a person's room 10 times in 12 hours, I would spend 45 minutes to one hour just getting dressed and undressed. Since we were assigned at least eight patients on the night shift, you can see how impractical it was to try to save time. These gowns were designed to be single-use only. Except at this time, gowns had to be reused since there weren't enough to go around. It was imperative—as in "I'm-not-joking-you-really-have-to-do-this-if-you've-got-a-lick-of-infection-control-sense"—to put on and take off gowns in the proper order so as to not contaminate yourself and your scrubs.

Then there was short staffing. Nurses were contracting COVID-19, which led to a more severe staffing shortage than we'd had before the pandemic. Around the first of May, Trail State University Health Care decided to use travel nurses to shore up staffing within the entire system. I had to say that—other than that I wished the hospital would pay me what they were paying the traveling nurses (about three times my usual salary)—these men and women were lifesaving angels. These were very competent nurses who worked every bit as hard and as skillfully as our regular TMH bedside nurses. Thanks to their help, by about mid-May, I wasn't fighting the urge to have a panic attack on the way to work. We enjoyed a period of about two months of good-enough staffing until traveling nurses were removed from the budget and staff nurses began quitting and getting sick again.

The final issue was the acuity level of COVID-19 patients. Our patients were not on ventilators. Some of them had decided they didn't want ventilators at all. Monitoring high-flow oxygen devices, lab tests, and proning were never-ending. It was not possible to simply go into a room, fluff a pillow, check the oxygen, do a physical assessment, check the tubings, give a medication, flip the person onto their back or belly, say some general therapeutic words, and go onto the next person until the next time I was able to visit. Patients were very scared, and family members weren't physically present but were often on the phone or a tablet. Answering questions and offering reassurance included the family, whether they were in the parking lot or at home. If a person chose not to be on a ventilator and was close to death, most of us were faced with an honest-to-goodness ethical dilemma: Should I stay in the room and support the dying patient? Or check on my other very sick patients and possibly avoid their death?

I had this dilemma with Penny Grayton. Remember her?

Penny had been on 3 North with septicemia at the very beginning of the pandemic. She was a delightful woman in her early 80s, living at Water's Edge Assisted Living and Rehabilitation Center. She'd contracted COVID-19 despite the isolation of residents that Water's Edge had implemented. She'd been placed on 3 North because she didn't want a ventilator. As she put it, "I've lived a long time, and to be honest, earthly life doesn't have a whole lot to recommend it, especially when you're my age."

I remembered Penny as the patient who'd introduced me to urban fantasy as a literary genre. These are books where a world is under siege from evil forces and the hero saves the day. Penny had taught me that the trick in these books was to discover the villain's weakness and destroy their dastardly power. Penny's grandson had introduced her to these books, and his name was Rhett—I remembered that because Gone With The Wind was the first movie I saw where I fell madly in love with a character, Rhett Butler. I'm not sure if he was the hero or the villain, but he was heart-stopping gorgeous to my early adolescent self.

Penny was recovering and doing well on high flow pressurized oxygen. She was talkative when I made initial rounds about 1945 (7:45 pm). Rhett and his parents, Penny's son, and daughter-in-law were taking turns visiting via a tablet. If you can imagine a family just sitting at the bedside, that's what it looked like, except on a tablet. Rhett was a bespeckled young man. He looked to be in his middle teens. Rhett's mom, Monica, looked perfectly normal, which deviated from Penny's earlier description of her as a bit pretentious. His dad, Steve, looked like a middle-aged guy. They didn't have questions for me except to ask that I take good care of Penny. I assured them I would and left to see my other seven patients.

Penny continued to be stable until about midnight. I noticed that her urine output dropped from a low but acceptable amount every two hours (60 milliliters) to less than five milliliters by midnight. I flushed the catheter to see if it was plugged; it was not. The hospital physician ordered labs and it was determined that her BUN and creatinine were sky-high. The morning lab studies were in the normal high range. The new findings indicated kidney failure.

Penny's pulse oximeter reading had also dropped between 76-81, which was dangerously low. She was not responding to an increase in pressured oxygen flow. I pushed her call button and asked if a respiratory therapist could come in and any available staff to help me turn Penny prone. She had medication ordered to help with feelings of breathlessness—the feeling of not being able to catch your breath was understandably very scary. Penny felt less breathless after the medication but was not improving. Her lung sounds were normal in the upper back. In her lower back or lung bases, her lungs sounded like Velcro being pulled apart. These sounds or crackles were heard throughout inspiration, and they indicated problems with oxygen exchange in the smallest airways, or alveoli. That was why kidney failure and pneumonia were common causes of death from COVID-19.

In about 15 minutes, two nurses, a unit clerk, and a respiratory therapist had put on PPE and assembled in the room. Penny weighed about 180 pounds and was 5 feet 2 inches tall, so turning her would take time and competence. We had her prone and more comfortable in another 40 minutes. It was nearing 1:30

am. Steve, Monica, and Rhett quietly observed us on the tablet. I didn't know what they could see, so I explained what we were doing at every step. When they saw she was more comfortable, they decided to take turns sleeping a few hours each. Steve was on the first "shift."

At 4:30 am, Steve and Monica changed places. I was in the room because Penny's cardiac telemetry monitor showed a heart rate of 50 and was dropping. I had the hospitalist physician paged. He came to the door and looked in, wearing an N95. I gave him a quick rundown of the last five hours.

"Go ahead with your palliative measures, Kit," he said. "Call me if you need anything."

Physicians rarely came into COVID rooms at this stage of the pandemic. There was not much they could do since treatment was almost all nursing care. Also, to be blunt, there were fewer doctors than nurses, and the hospital administration wanted to limit the doctors' exposure as much as possible.

There was nothing more we could do for Penny since she didn't want to be intubated. I could only keep her prone since she seemed to be in no distress and give her medication to help ease any pain or breathlessness she may develop.

Penny's level of consciousness was sleepy at this point, but I explained what was going on. She nodded. "Are you still okay with no ventilator?" I asked. She nodded again.

Keeping my gloved hand on her arm, I turned to the tablet. Monica and Steve were wide-eyed and silent.

"Steve," I said softly, "Your mom is dying." I waited. They both nodded and stayed silent. "Would you like me to place the tablet where you can see her face?" They nodded.

"Can you stay?" asked Monica.

"Let's see how she does," I said. "I'm here now." I know that sounded callous but promising to stay was not fair to them, my team, or my other patients. I pressed Penny's call button and asked if Tala could come to the door. Tala was the charge nurse.

She came to the door, walked in wearing a mask, and shut the door. I explained what was going on. She told me to stay with Penny while she checked my other patients.

A quick glance at Penny's monitors and observing her respiratory rate told both of us that time was running out. I touched Penny's shoulder and called her name. She was not responding. Tala left.

I moved the tablet so that Monica and Steve were able to see Penny. Rhett had been awakened. "Please tell your mom and grandmother anything you'd like. She can hear you even though she isn't responding right now."

A couple of things went through my mind while Penny's family assured her of their love and prayers. At that moment, I felt gratitude for the Wi-Fi technology that allowed families to be together during a quarantine. I was also struck by how much harder this was for the families I cared for than it had been for those who died. We were all alone when we die, and it's been my experience that many people look forward to something more and better after death. Family members, though, were left to miss the person and grieve.

I moved to Penny's side. Her heart rate was fluctuating between 40 and 50. She fluttered her eyes.

Then I did something so against COVID policy that I would have been disciplined on the spot had it been known. I moved my face mask down so Penny could see my face. I said to her, "You are well-loved. Thank you for including me in your life. Steve, Rhett, and Monica are right here." The mask went back into place, and I removed a glove to place my hand on her skin. "I'm right here, too."

I checked my watch, and Penny died eight minutes later. Her family knew, but I affirmed her passing. I pushed Penny's call button and told the unit clerk to tell Tala.

"Stay as long as you'd like," I told the family. "Can you tell me which funeral home you'll be using? If you can call them, please, they will work with you. We will make sure Penny is clean and ready when they arrive. They know what to do."

"Kit," sobbed Steve. "Thank you for touching my mom when she died."

"Your mom was an important woman to many of us. It was my honor to care for her," I said honestly.

Walking to the door, my PPE came off in the correct sequence. You can also believe that my hand hygiene was superbly meticulous.

Chapter Thirty-Two

"Patriotism isn't enough. There must be
no hatred or bitterness for anyone."
                                    - Florence Nightingale

As May moved into June, there was still no proven treatment for COVID-19. Admissions continued to be high at TMH. Scientists and other people who fancied themselves to be COVID-19 fighting heroes and heroines worked at a fevered pitch. New ideas and possible cures were being reported every day.

Of course, technology in the form of social media continued its love/hate relationship with the public. Any news that didn't suit some people was termed "fake," and a finding that suited others was considered the Rosetta Stone. That is to say, depending on your perspective, the same information was analyzed by some news and entertainment sites as having malicious intent and by other platforms as the key to COVID's previously unexplained mysteries.

I was reminded of a quote attributed to Mark Twain: "If you don't read the newspapers, you're uninformed. If you read the newspapers, you're misinformed."

Context is everything.

I got caught up in this, too. I became aware that more and more people needed to be the ones with the right answers. At all costs. The right side of "truth" wasn't easy to understand. Cynicism was widespread. The ability to belittle people who disagreed with you was elevated to a place of admiration. The need to be the person with the right answer became paramount.

Even at work, patients would talk about how they'd stopped talking to family members who had a "wrong" perspective. I started to feel uncomfortable offering an opinion about anything remotely controversial.

Here is an example of how it hit me between the eyes. One night, I brought leftovers for lunch. A physician saw me eating warmed-up sweet and sour chicken and accused me of being un-American. What? Chinese food was now un-American? I was so shocked, I laughed. Wrong move. He told me that if I didn't support the U.S., I might as well move to a country that liked my radical views.

I'm not going to kid you—that scared me. I was not a great thinker when it came to emotional topics, and it was easy to drag me into the fray. Was I wrong about COVID-19? Was I really not able to think through right and wrong using my values? Were my values a threat to myself and others?

I did have the triple-headers to talk to. Gram and Harrison and Dad helped me see both sides of the huge divide. Thanks to them, I was able to be less concerned with knowing everything than being all right with learning as COVID-19 unfolded. It was Gram who helped me remember that I forgot a few basic principles of scientific discovery.

As she reminded me, scientists knew more about cellular biology and immunology than I'd ever understand. COVID-19 was in a family of viruses that immunologists had battled before. They also deciphered the genome DNA code of this coronavirus a few months ago. Scientists were not working blind.

The second, and probably most important, was the need to test a treatment and review test results. A hunch is not a fact, and one study or one person's experience can't be trusted to work for everyone. Listen for insight. Call it what you will, but it's part of the equation. Hope. Curiosity. Awareness. Prayer.

Some of the early proposed treatments were logical, but just not correct. Some were flat-out dangerous but didn't prevent a certain degree of professional and lay buy-in.

I was reminded of something I learned in my history of nursing course. Hippocrates, who is often considered the father of western medicine wrote, "For extreme diseases, extreme methods of cure, as to restriction, are most suitable." The modern interpretation of this expression might be "desperate times call for desperate measures." Restricting contact with others was desperate, but Hippocrates might say, "most suitable."

In May, the first antiviral drug, remdesivir, was approved for emergency use with COVID019 patients. Supplies were scarce, and so it was originally given only to the very sickest patients. Later on, remdesivir was found to work best if given early in the course of the disease, but that discovery only came after…yep, more testing.

At TMH, we just kept keeping on. By mid-May, businesses were reopening. I was working less overtime.

My social life improved with the weather. Tala and I saw each other more frequently, which was fun. She cooked and I baked, so we ate well and laughed a lot.

Also: romance alert! Harrison and I started to look at each other differently. You could say we started dating. Things were looking up.

Chapter Thirty-Three

**"It's easier to fool people than to convince
people they've been fooled."**

- Mark Twain

On the nights I didn't work, I usually stayed up until about 4
am. Then, I slept until noon. Even if I had to work again the
next night, my sleep cycle wasn't thrown off.

Linda Ackerman and I continued our baking classes via
technology. Since I worked with COVID-19 patients and since
Mark didn't believe in masks, we decided to work together without being together.

We used a variety of platforms. If something was especially
tricky, we used Zoom so I could see and imitate her. I ended up
needing that when making tomato pie, which was such a delicious mixture of fresh tomatoes and cheese and fabulous spices!
The first time, she coached me over speaker phone. She told me
how to adapt the pie crust and admonished me to "make sure
the tomatoes are very dry." It came out like tomato soup…with
bread. I didn't understand what "very dry" meant for the tomatoes. It was delicious but could never be served to other people.
So, another evening, we used Zoom, and the pie came out beau-
tifully. I was pumped.

That morning at around 2:00 a.m. I was enjoying my second
generous piece of tomato pie and watching *Hamilton* on Disney
Plus as happy as anything. Then, a banging started at my door.

"Kit! Are you up? Kit! Open up! Help!"

I grabbed my Maddy mask and opened the door. It was Linda. "Kit, it's Mark. He can't breathe. He's had a fever and cough all day and won't let me call the doctor. Now he's in his recliner and I can hear him breathing across the room. What should I do?"

I had my phone in my hand and called 911. The estimated arrival time was about five minutes, which was a miracle in itself. There had been so many EMS calls during COVID that the system was overloaded. Harrison had told me that a paramedic told him that 30 minutes was about the average wait time. Not exactly firsthand information, but it made sense.

I walked to their door and into the great room. I could see Mark from a safe distance. He was struggling to breathe but was still able to talk.

"Mark, it's Kit. Can you hear me?"

"Yes."

"Mark, the paramedics are on their way. Can you sit up a little straighter? Linda can help you."

"That's better."

"Mark, I'm not going to come much closer since my best filtering mask is at the hospital. But I'm not going to leave. I'll keep an eye on you, and if I have to, I promise I'll come closer. Is that okay with you?"

"Okay. What's. The. Matter?"

"My guess is that you have COVID, but I'm not sure. COVID-19 is very contagious. Let's just act like you have COVID until you get to the hospital. That's why I'm staying across the room from you."

"His lodge buddy died a week ago from COVID," Linda told me. "They had a memorial at the lodge three or four days ago. None of the other guys are sick."

"Dammit, Linda," Mark wheezed. "Shut up about the lodge. No one got sick at the lodge. John died at the hospital. Not the lodge."

Although Mark's logic was faulty beyond belief, the fact that he could still talk enough to yell at his wife gave me reassurance that he was oxygenating all right for now.

"I should have killed him when I had the chance," Linda muttered. "I'd be out by now." She looked at Mark and sighed. "Oh, Kit, I didn't mean that really."

EMS came through the door dressed in full PPE and did what they call a "scoop and run." Mark's vital signs were taken, cardiac monitor and pulse oximeter patches applied, an IV started, and a high-flow non-pressure oxygen mask applied. Linda gave his name, date of birth, allergies, and phone number. A paramedic told her she couldn't come to the hospital, but she would be called for insurance information. Mark was lifted onto a gurney, and they were gone. From the elevator, I heard one of them say, "Time in 2:19. Time out 2:25." Six minutes. Wow.

I stayed with Linda, keeping my distance until she called her son in San Davers. It sounded as though he'd woken up quickly and would leave within 30 minutes to drive to Thompson.

I made coffee and helped Linda find all of Mark's medications and his insurance card. The call from the hospital went smoothly, and Linda was told that they would call her later with updates. Linda was told Mark had consented to intubation and a ventilator if necessary.

True to his word, Mark Jr. arrived in less than two and one-half hours. He nodded at me and offered me an elbow bump greeting.

"Hi, call me Junior. You're Kit, right? Thank you so much." He went straight to Linda and enveloped her in a hug.

She finally cried. "I was so scared. What if he dies?"

While waiting for Junior, I went home and grabbed four Maddy masks. Since Linda had direct exposure, she and Junior agreed to wear them around the house for at least five days. Linda and Junior each had two masks: one to wear and one to wash. We discussed how to sanitize surfaces and bedding that Mark had come in contact with.

"I'm leaving now, Linda," I said. "I'm right across the hall if you need anything. Anything at all."

She nodded and started to get up.

"Please don't get up. Let's just keep our distance to be safe, okay? I'll be home until tomorrow night. I'm off again tonight. Call anytime. If I don't answer, I'm sleeping. If it's an emergency, come over and pound on the door."

I threw her a masked kiss and left. It was almost 6 am. I showered, washed my hair, put all my clothes and my Maddy mask in the laundry, and crashed into bed.

Chapter Thirty-Four

**"If we were meant to talk more than listen,
we'd have two mouths and one ear."**
- Mark Twain

Junior knocked on my door a little after noon. When I got out of bed and opened the door, he backed away about six feet to talk. Mark had died in the Emergency Department a few minutes before. He wanted to let me know and thanked me again. He and Linda were calling the family. They would stay in touch.

I went straight to the cupboard and pulled out a double chocolate brownie mix. I added chocolate chips and extra eggs. When it had cooled, I cut three pieces for myself and took 12 pieces on a paper plate over to Linda and Junior. Sometimes the only thing that makes any sense is chocolate.

Chapter Thirty-Five

"I think one's feelings waste themselves in words.
They should be distilled into action."
- Florence Nightingale

Harrison, Tala, and I met for lunch or dinner at my apartment at least once a week. We had great camaraderie.

Here was our routine: we would meet at the community food bank for either the "morning shift" if it was Tuesday or the "afternoon shift" if it was Thursday. We would be assigned to be a packer or a loader. Packers would fill boxes with donated canned goods, bread, and fresh fruits and vegetables. Loaders would place the boxes into the cars that came. Loaders had limited contact with our "customers." One person took names as a record for the state Food Assistance Program. Then, cars pulled up to the door. Volunteers loaded the cars, gave a quick rundown of what was in the box this week, and said goodbye with a masked wave...from at least six feet away.

I was astonished at the number of cars we saw every week. In each shift, at least fifty cars lined up around the perimeter of the parking lot. At least. One day in early June, we packed 100 boxes, and all were placed in cars by the team of loaders. There was most certainly a food shortage for some families in Thompson.

The kindness shown to others by the donors and volunteers was comforting to me. Regardless of the mean-spiritedness that seemed to permeate the news, there were helpers of every stripe who showed up every week. Except for Tala and Harrison, none of the other volunteers worked at TMH. Even though we were masked and distanced, my contact with the outside world was improving.

After we finished, we would meet at my place. If it was a holy day or a saint's day, Tala would attend mass and meet us later. Tala had changed since our furlough time in San Davers. Since living around the sisters for those three weeks, she now attended mass regularly. A teacher was needed for online classes for second graders who were preparing for First Communion, and Tala volunteered. Her language was still colorful, and her views of the world were still through a passionate lens. She didn't suffer fools gladly but hadn't gone over the holiness hill. She was still Tala, only more settled.

It seemed there were a lot of saints' days, so usually Harrison and I were alone for an hour or so until Tala arrived. I really liked Harrison. He was a smart and very nice guy.

I had been struggling with the uncertainty of the pandemic. There was so much unknown and so little consensus that I was feeling lost. It turned out that Harrison felt the same.

"Of course, we feel lost," he said. "We've never been in a time like this before."

Being with Harrison made me believe that I could be patient with not knowing enough right now.

We talked about positive things: the weather that allowed people outside, cases coming down a little bit, and some newer therapies that seemed to be working. Fewer people were dying of COVID-19.

We talked about ways we could support families grieving the loss of loved ones or jobs or social interaction. Harrison always took time to knock on Linda's door and spend a few minutes alone with her to talk about Mark and her new life as a widow.

As we discovered through our conversations, we both liked historical fiction and authors who wrote well-researched books like James Michener and Ken Follett.

Truth be told, I was always happy for a saint's day because Harrison and I could spend time alone. Our work schedules were so full that we only saw each other socially once a week.

At Harrison's request, we decided to see if our friendship and mutual attraction could stand the test of actual dating. Harrison was a wonderful man as well as a high-quality kisser. He had nice shoulders to lean on literally and figuratively.

But enough waxing poetic about Harrison. You get the drift.

Now that businesses had opened up, we often had Tala pick up take-out at our favorite restaurant. It was next door to her church and on her way. Harrison and Tala and I liked both Italian food and Chinese food. Lucky for us, Thompson has Tony Liu's, the best Italian/Chinese restaurant ever. Their décor is not as startling as you might imagine, given the different cultures and cuisines. They used red, green, and gold to create a delightful atmosphere. Tony Liu's was not yet open for dine-in, but we could always find something for take-out. No matter what we felt like eating, there was always something on Tony Liu's menu.

One day when we were waiting for Tala to bring lunch, Harrison told me that Linda's grandson was coming to live with her. Mark's death had been tough for her. Living alone wasn't for everyone, and Linda hated it. This grandson hadn't gone back to work in an actual place. He was working online and so could live anywhere.

"He's supposed to arrive today so you might see him around. Before I leave, maybe we can knock on the door and meet him."

The lobby buzzer sounded, and I let Tala in. She wafted in a lovely cloud of garlic. It didn't take much time for us to load up our plates and start eating.

When I'd moved into my apartment at Chateau Bordeaux, my friend Hannah had contributed to my bare apartment. She and her mom had given me the family discount at the Antique and Consignment Shop they owned together. I couldn't believe that honest-to-goodness real sets of china were available for next to nothing. Place settings for 12! Serving pieces, too! Apparently, no one used fine china anymore. Well, I did, and my "everyday" dishes were from an English company. They had pale blue flowers on the border and were trimmed with platinum. Dishwasher safe, too! Not to be too boastful, but my dishes were classy.

We were talking and eating when Harrison got a text. "It's from Linda. Apparently, little Mark is here and wants to come over to say hello."

"Little Mark?" I said. "Doesn't that family have any male name imagination? There was Linda's Mark, Junior Mark, and now Little Mark. Sure. If it's okay with you two, send him over."

Less than five minutes later, there was a strong knock on my door.

"He must have been poised at the door," laughed Tala.

I grabbed a Maddy mask and opened the door. The guy standing in front of me was wearing a designer jogging outfit and just-out-of-the-box-I-bet-they-cost-as-much-as-I-make-in-a-day-before-taxes athletic shoes. His smile changed to shock.

"You!" I said. "You never told me your last name was Ackerman!"

"It never came up. You never told me you lived in this great place."

"It never came up. Didn't the name Kit ring a bell? How many Kits do you know? Little Mark, huh? Original. Where's your mask?"

"Right here. My dad gave me one of your homemade ones. Nana washed it. Shouldn't you put yours on over both ears?"

It was Mark from San Davers. Exercise Mark. ATP tattoo Mark. Mark the Pescatarian. No Social Skills Mark. Really Hunky and Hot Mark.

Jeez Louise.

Chapter Thirty-Six

"Never take or give an excuse."
-Florence Nightingale

Little Mark from San Davers and I were at a standoff in the hallway. I'm not sure who was more surprised to see the other.

"Hi, I'm Tala. Do you know each other?"

I looked at Tala, who was standing next to me, and Harrison, who was on his feet at our lunch plates. They looked like they had just walked into the best part of a movie.

"We met in San Davers. Mark was Erin's exercise coach," I said by way of explanation.

Mark peered over my shoulder. "We were in a social bubble together. And I'm a lifestyle coach. Health is more than exercise. Are you still doing the breathing and stretching moves we practiced?" he asked me in that tone of voice that I remembered so well. It made me want to alternately slap him and force-feed him a chocolate bar—and a milk chocolate bar, not healthy dark chocolate.

"Only you could make a social bubble and exercise sound obscene," I muttered.

Suddenly the absurdity of the situation hit me, and I started to laugh. "You might as well come in. We do wear masks if you're not part of our regular social group, so we'll put them on until you leave. We wear the 'homemade' ones at home, too."

Harrison moved over and let Little Mark sit on the dining bench.

"So, do you want something?" I asked in my most hospitable tone.

"Like what?" L.M. asked.

"Like, did you want to get to the point of your impromptu visit?" I countered.

"My Nana said the nurse across the hall has been so helpful to her since my Papa passed away. She enjoys teaching the nurse to bake and that her boyfriend is very nice, too," he said and smiled at Harrison, who seemed to be having a great time listening to this conversation. "I probably should have paid more attention to the name of the nurse. Haha! Didn't you make some Scottish bread when you were staying with Erin and Mary? Was that Nana's recipe?"

"It's Irish soda bread. How long are you staying? With your Nana, I mean," I asked.

"Well, my exercise and nutrition classes are all online now, so I don't have to be back at any particular time. I've started cooking classes and they've been crazy successful. I told Matt I'd still pay my share of the rent. So, I'm here until I choose to go, or Nana kicks me out."

"Wow. That's quite a story," I said.

His eyes crinkled above his mask. He was grinning at my other guests. I just knew it. "Your name is Tala, right?"

She nodded.

"That's a Native American name, right? Doesn't it mean 'wolf'?"

"It's interesting that you know one of the meanings of my name," said Tala. "Tala means wolf in some Indian languages. There are over 600 languages among Native American tribes. My mother was a Choctaw. Tala means 'Leaping Waters' in her dialect."

Tala had never told me the meaning of her name, and I thought we were good friends. More to the point, how did he know such an obscure fact? This was turning into one weird lunch.

"Fascinating," said Dictionary Mark. "Your hair is so straight and pure black. I'm sorry to be personal this early in our friendship, but you're simply beautiful."

"Thank you, Mark," said Tala. "It's very nice to meet you."

"Are you a full-blooded Indian? What do you people like to be called? Indian? Native American?" asked Mark, leaning in toward Tala.

Now that's the social idiot Mark I know! What do *you people* like to be called? I mentally rubbed my hands together with glee. You're going down Mark, I thought.

But Tala just laughed. "Well, I don't think anyone has ever been that direct with me. My people would be fine with either one. What do you people like to be called? You're European American, right? Do you prefer 'immigrant' or just 'white guy'?"

Little Mark looked properly chastised. "Oh, I'm sorry. Sometimes I'm terribly uncouth."

"Hells Bells, Mark, it's okay. I'll help you adjust your vulgarities. I have some colorful language habits, too. We can work on public discourse skills together."

What the actual fu...funky? Tala should be cleaning his clock right now, not inviting him into her life. I looked over at Harrison, whose eyes were following the conversation like he was at a Wimbledon match. He was loving this.

"Well, I'd better go," said L.M. "Kit, if you'd be open to this idea, I'd like to be part of your social bubble again."

I felt as though I'd been propositioned, and right in front of my new boyfriend. "Well," I said.

"I don't plan to socialize outside Nana's house, and she doesn't go anywhere without a mask these days. I'd be glad to wait the recommended 10 days to be sure I'm healthy enough for your group."

"That's very considerate of you, Mark," said Harrison. "We'll include you in our next lunch or dinner in two weeks."

"That's lit," he said. "Thanks. Bye now."

He walked himself to the door and left.

"What a schmuck," I said, failing to hit the right slang note that L.M. did.

"I like him," said Tala.

"He's okay," said Harrison. "Although I must say that you and he were pretty quick on the repartee. Were you close friends in San Davers?"

"No," I said.

"Me thinks thou dost protest too much," said Harrison, paraphrasing Shakespeare.

"Yep," said Tala. "Your denial is quite strong. Could you possibly mean the opposite?"

I love my friends. Yes, Mark got under my skin. Tala and Harrison knew my foibles and liked me anyway.

"Oh, you guys," I said. "Maybe I wasn't the most gracious host. But do you really want to include him in our group?"

"He's cute. I'd be okay with that," said Tala. "It's almost 3. I'm picking up an extra six hours tonight and need a nap. Thanks for a fun lunch."

After Tala left, Harrison and I sat on the couch and got to know each other better for a while. He didn't bring up the possibility of Mark joining our lunch/dinner group. Neither did I.

As he was leaving, he cupped my face in his hands and kissed my forehead. "Bye, my Kit. I love you."

Chapter Thirty-Seven

"What cruel mistakes are sometimes made by benevolent
men and women in matters of business about which they
can know nothing and think they know a great deal."
                                                    - Florence Nightingale

Things came to a head at work the week before Memorial
Day. Supplies were scarce again, but this time, the rationale
was not supply chain issues but cost containment.

The supply of disposable gowns had freed up and we had
an adequate number available to us. But for some reason, Dr.
Weaver and his bunch of administrators were under the impression that nurses didn't really need to use disposable gowns once
and then, you know, dispose of them.

In May, we started having weekly video "chats." Every
week a different administrator recorded a "chat." They were 10
minutes in length and available all week long on the employee
website. New chats were released at 12:30 am every Monday
morning. The overall theme was "TMH is Crushing COVID."

Chat was such a misleading term. No one was really chat-
ting with the administrator of the week. It was a carefully orches-
trated presentation.

Since this day was Monday, Tala and I were able to listen to
the newest presentation while I took my lunch and a 15-minute
break at 3:00 am.

The chat administrator this week was the man in charge of
Infection Control Services. He congratulated us all on keeping the

spread of COVID down within the ranks of RNs. We had done such a good job that the number of nurses who'd actually developed COVID-19 at TMH was under the anticipated percentage. But that wasn't the best news, he said. The bottom line (no pun intended) was that meant that our crisis PPE policies were fine. Since the pandemic was still going strong, we didn't need to rush to meet professional infection control standards of care. We needed to continue to be careful of our supply costs. He ended his presentation by thanking all nurses and other clinical staff for representing TMH so well. "You are heroes," he said pointing his forefinger at the screen. "Don't forget it." "Do me a favor," I said to Tala. "Don't ever call me a hero." "Ditto," she said.

After Shift Report, Tala pointed out an administrator walking into the unit. She was on 3 North to do what was termed "making safety rounds." In retrospect, I supposed I should have felt sorry for her. She didn't know Tala and I had just seen the latest chat. Unfortunately, too, she'd obviously missed the class in hospital administration school called: "Look sincere enough that nurses will think you're concerned about a safe work environment, but really, safety comes after profit."

Her name was blackened out on her name badge, which seemed to be a reasonable strategic decision. After all, she was about to become a sacrificial lamb for her colleagues. She was a slim 20-something woman with a fresh haircut and manicure. She wore a black mask with TMH in bling, a name tag that told us whomever she was had an MBA, and heels so tall that if she fell, we'd need an X-ray to check for fracture.

Her task this day on 3 North was counting the N95 masks and making sure we weren't indiscriminately using large numbers of them to prevent COVID virus transfer. We did very well at keeping the cost of masks down, and she wanted us to be proud that we were supporting TMH.

One nurse asked her why the supply of disposable gowns had been cut. She reminded the administrator that professional standards were meant to be adhered to and that the word "standard" meant basic obligation for safe practice. The administrator countered by explaining that "professional standards" were "suggestions," not really "requirements."

That was where she made her mistake. She made that proclamation in front of Tala.

Tala and I were heading out of the unit. Once we got through the double doors, Tala told me to go ahead. She was going to the administration office to speak to our corporate nursing officer, Stephanie Porter.

I did not go ahead. I went with Tala. Although I'm not as articulate as Tala, I had had it with making do with under-budget staffing and inadequate supplies. I was going to be her wing nurse.

We were told that Dr. Porter and Dr. Weaver were in a meeting. We said we'd wait. The administrative assistant let us sit for about 30 minutes. When she saw we weren't going anywhere, she started to glance nervously at the door to the corporate suite of offices.

Her options were limited. We were quiet and patient, so calling security to have us removed was out of the question. She seemed an experienced admin, which meant she'd probably figured out we weren't there to wish Drs. Porter and Weaver a pleasant day. We were there with a problem.

After an hour, the poor woman walked into the C-suite and returned looking relieved. If we would be willing to wait until 9:30 am, then both administrators could see us together. However, she knew that we worked nights and were probably exhausted. She would be glad to give us an appointment early next week.

Tala looked at me. "You don't have to stay."

"I'm picking up six extra hours tonight, but not until midnight, so I'm fine right here," I said.

"We will wait," Tala told the Admin.

"I'll let them know," she said.

At 9:50 am, we were escorted into Dr. Weaver's office. He sat behind a handsome desk and asked what he might do for us ladies today.

Let me stop here and interject that Tala is cool under pressure. She didn't raise her voice or whine. She plainly and calmly laid out our concerns.

There were significant staffing issues. Unless we had traveling nurses, we were working one or two nurses under budget every night shift. We understood and appreciated the occasional use of traveling nurses. We also appreciated the overtime pay we received since we were working over 40 hours every week. We even understood that this overtime wasn't mandatory. However, when Tala was not able to work an extra six hours last pay period, she was told by the night supervisor that her inability to fully commit to the COVID crisis would be remembered at her annual evaluation.

Tala looked at me, and I picked up on the topic of this week's chat. Infection control standards were not being met under the guise of cost containment during a crisis. The supplies were in the hospital in storage, but not available for use by nurses. The impression given was that infection control standards were optional, not mandatory.

Tala nodded. "You see, Dr. Porter and Dr. Weaver, we want to do well for our patients. That's why we do this kind of work. We are not so uninformed that we don't appreciate the need to watch the budget. Nurses get it. 'No money, no mission' is a well-understood and true colloquialism. We can't do our work if we don't have enough money. I guess I'm most frustrated when I learn that the hospital board approved a 2.5-million-dollar bonus to be paid to you, Dr. Weaver, Dr. Porter, and three other administrators at TMH. And yet, we're counting $1 masks on the nursing units.

"Where did you hear that?" asked Dr. Weaver. I presumed he meant his bonus, not the cost of masks.

"It's in the hospital board minutes that were quoted yesterday in the newspaper," said Tala.

"Well, I can understand your frustrations. Let me just say that Dr. Stephanie and I will personally look into each of these concerns. Hospital budgets are tricky and often confusing. For example, using traveling nurses for every open position is simply not feasible. The costs are not sustainable. I know you nurses have it rough. You are my heroes. COVID-19 was such an unanticipated event. Preparation for every possible health crisis sounds simple, but believe me, it's not possible." He shrugged and gave a very good approximation expression of torment.

"Do you think traveling nurses would cost 2.5 million dollars during the immediate crisis?" asked Tala.

Dr. Weaver actually chuckled. "Oh, if only it was that simple. We'd all be in hog heaven."

Dr. Stephanie sat looking at Dr. Weaver as if she wished CEO stupidity was a capital offense. "I understand completely, Tala and Kit. Please let me look at the numbers again. I promise you I'll get back to you," she said.

Dr. Weaver stood up. "Well, if there's nothing else, I'll let us all get on with our day. Thank you for coming in, umm…"

We stood.

"Tala Denton," Tala said. "My name is Tala Denton. Remember my name. You'll be screaming it later."

We walked out of the mahogany-lined hallway and back into the waiting room. Politely thanking the admin for her assistance, we left the C-suite and pushed the elevator button. Once in the elevator, I nearly fell into Tala.

"Can you believe that bull? Can you?" I asked. "At least we're his heroes."

Tala grinned. "I've been waiting for my whole career to use that quote from Florence Nightingale: 'You'll be screaming my name later.'"

"Stephanie looked mad enough to spit. Maybe we'll actually get a response," I said. "What's with that bonus? How do they sleep at night?"

We laughed at Tala's cleverness and waved goodbye in the parking lot.

As I climbed into my Civic, I remembered what my patient Penny Grayton said about urban fantasy literature. The trick to saving the world from annihilation was figuring out who were the villains and what their weakness was. It had to do with a fear of kittens. The bad guys were afraid of kittens.

Where could I lay my hands on some kittens and let them loose in the C-suite?

Chapter Thirty-Eight

R-Squared: Rock My World Ruminations

I'll be so glad when I can see my family again. A family picnic will be this weekend at Mom and Dad's house to celebrate Kai's graduation. All activities will be outside and for only two hours. We will all wear masks except for eating. No hugging allowed. Mandy and I will be there to monitor the six-feet-apart rule. I'm bringing my homemade hand sanitizer for everyone. My favorite online store had some cute little plastic bottles, so everyone will have their own. Thank you to the State Department of Health website for the sanitizer recipe.

Work is still busy but less horrible since the census of COVID-19 patients is dropping a little due to more people involved in outside activities.

Our CNO Stephanie Porter did do some things since the Tala vs. Dr. Weaver meeting. Hospital administrators are no longer checking old N95 masks to be sure they're dirty enough to warrant a new one. We're still counting masks since piracy is apparently a real thing. Some employees were taking N95 masks home, which put the hospital's supply at risk.

The traveling nurses' budget was approved for another month. Now, we usually only work one nurse short on nights.

No one in the C-suites gave back their bonuses. Tala had been philosophic: "Hell, sometimes we have to be happy with baby steps," she said.

Speaking of Tala, get this: she traded some nights and had a five-day off stretch. She said she needed some time outside Thompson. While she was gone, she didn't answer texts and didn't attend our virtual Sip and Stitch meeting.

Tala went back to the convent! She wants to be a nun! I guess it's called being a religious sister, not a nun because the Cherubim and Angels aren't a cloistered order. Whatever—this Lutheran didn't get it exactly. Nun. No Fun. That's what I say it sounds like. She went to a four-day retreat as part of the sign-up process. She's back now, and the only thing she'll say is that she needs to discern her calling. Not sure exactly what that means, but honestly? She seems content. Not thrilled or happy. Just content. Her language hasn't changed much. She still writes letters to the newspaper about nurse staffing at TMH and pleads with the public to stay safe. She wrote an article about her experiences as a staff nurse during COVID-19 and submitted it to a nursing journal for possible publication. She's the same except for the possibility of joining up with SAC. Can you believe it?

Graduation was canceled at Thompson High, which was the main reason for our backyard party. Kai will wear his cap and gown, and Mom is making a graduation cake. Mom is relieved that school finished right after Memorial Day. She hasn't said anything about going back next year. Teddy is teaching summer school online. Since his summer job as a mover with Two Buffs and A Truck is still on hold, he's just enjoying some time off.

Gram is coming to the party. Cannot wait to see her. Her thoughtful, common-sense approach to nursing continues to keep me on track.

Little Mark is like a fly you can't swat. He's been buzzing around and has embraced being part of our social circle. Harrison likes him and they play chess together.

Mark just shrugged when I told him about Tala's nun experiment "If that brings her happiness, she should go for it," he said. Did he know where she was going before she left town?

Harrison is becoming dearer to me every time I see him. He gives and gives to others, and always has time for me. I'm falling in love.

Diane from Sip and Stitch said "Wait until you find out his foibles. They all have foibles. Men!" I will not go to Diane if I have a Harrison question or concern.

Chapter Thirty-Nine

"So never lose an opportunity of urging a practical
beginning, however small, for it is wonderful how often in
such matters the mustard-seed germinates and roots itself."
- Florence Nightingale

Harrison and Tala had both been approved by Mom and Dad
to go to the graduation party. They understood the COVID
restrictions, and both were thrilled to be invited.

Now for the best part: The party. It was very normal.
Normal WAS underrated. I wanted it back again.

The party was all about Kai. He wore his cap and gown
for about an hour. At Dad's direction, we all hummed "Pomp
and Circumstance." When our music ended, Kai flipped his cap
tassel from the right to the left side, signifying he had officially
graduated!

Things had been mildly celebratory with Kai's class. There
was no prom, Senior trip, or in-person graduation ceremony. On
the day before graduation was originally scheduled, there had
been a virtual face-to-face call for anyone who signed in with
the link. All the graduates had their names read. The mayor gave
some words of congratulations, and the three valedictorians
gave short speeches. Kai was not a valedictorian, but he graduated with a perfectly fine GPA and plans to go to TSU next year.

There was a car parade on the day graduation was originally scheduled. The Thompson School Board chose the day and
time for graduates to meet in their cars in the school parking lots.

All four lots were full. Invites to the class were communicated on Twitter and Facebook. Some teachers and the principal were there. At precisely noon, loudspeakers played the Thompson Tigers fight song and car horns blared for two full minutes. Two minutes for the Class of 2020. Every graduate got a goodie bag with items donated by the parent's club and local businesses. Nobody got out of their car. It sounded corny, but Kai loved it.

Tala went to mass before the party, so we knew she'd be late. Mom was bringing out the cake when she arrived. She brought Mark with her! Little Mark! Who'd invited him? It turns out that mom did when Tala called and asked her if she could bring him. Since he's part of our social bubble, Mom thought it was OK. I knew that Tala was encouraged by the sisters to date as part of her decision to join the nunhood which I thought was a very sensible idea. Tala's choice of a man to date needed some refinement. Maybe since he's in our social bubble, she probably figured "any port in a storm." If I had to date Mark, I'd be sure to seriously consider religious life as an alternative.

Gram was carrying out the ice cream and stopped in her tracks.

"Oh my gosh! Hi, Mark," she said. "I haven't seen you lately and didn't know you knew my family."

"Oh, Jennifer, I was hoping you'd be here. When Kit was in San Davers, she mentioned your name, but I didn't break our confidentiality agreement," said Mark.

"Oh, wow. Jennifer and Mark together again!" said Mandy. She turned and looked at me with my mouth agape. "I guess maybe we owe some explanations. Let's cut the cake first. Gram and Mark's story is very cool."

We all got Kai's favorite marble cake and vanilla ice cream and sat in our safely distanced seats.

Here's the long and short of it. My Gram and Little Mark met a few weeks after COVID-19 was declared a national emergency. A request was placed in newspapers, Facebook, LinkedIn, and Twitter asking for volunteers to trial a vaccine when one was developed. The pharmaceutical company making the request was Mandy's, and she was in charge of the project. The federal project Warp Speed strongly supported rapid vaccine development. Gram and Mark had volunteered and had been participating in preliminary work prior to the Phase III trials.

Phase III trials were when a medication or vaccine is trialed with actual human subjects. There was a lot of work that went on before vaccines were tested on people. Phase I and Phase II trials were where the safe, effective dose and probable side effects was learned. New medications or vaccines aren't allowed to be used with people until Phase I and II trials are finished.

Phase III trials have half of the participants receiving no vaccine and half receiving the vaccine. Nobody knows who got the vaccine and who got the placebo or saltwater injection until the results were known. That's called "blinded." Blinding was one way to prevent cheating on reporting results. When effectiveness and side effects were evaluated, the groups were unblinded. That happens at the very end of the study. This was siesta information for most people, but there you have it anyway.

Gram and Mark had been part of regular virtual meetings to get ready. They had been tested for certain conditions. Their medical history was checked in detail. There were 20 people in their group, and they got to be friends. Scientific studies like these were kept quiet, and there weren't a lot of places to find information about them. Volunteers were asked to keep their participation private until the drugs were close to coming to federal approval.

Mandy wasn't sure (she said) when the Phase III trials would begin, but we were all excited to personally know such courageous people.

Mandy was emphatic that were not to tell others that we found out about this; there was too much controversy. Besides, we really didn't have much to tell. We only knew for sure that

Little Mark and Gram were meeting online with a group interested in COVID-19 vaccines.

My opinion of Mark kept improving. Too bad he was such a social doofus.

Mom kept us to the two-hour limit and sent us home through the gate, not the house. I had a million questions for Tala and Mark and Gram. How could they keep this a secret from me? Were these trials going to put Gram at any serious risk? Were Tala and Mark really dating-dating?

Harrison came over for a few hours after the party. We hashed over the secret Phase III trial information and played Scrabble. I spent time wondering out loud about Tala and Mark. Harrison said to leave it alone; apparently, it was none of my business. What the hell you say!

The next night, Tala and I were working together. I planned to grab her before Shift Report and see if I could get more of the skinny. I kept my fingers crossed for my interrogation success.

Chapter Forty

R-Squared: Resilience Ruminations

Today is the 4th of July. Independence Day in the United States. Last night was blessedly uneventful on 3 North. Fingers crossed for tonight. I need my ruminations so I can sleep.

Since the beginning of this year, every part of my life has changed. I've spent time learning how to cope with job insecurity. Taking steps to check out any available opportunities to work if something like a pandemic puts a temporary halt in income was the key to avoiding dipping into savings.

I enjoyed my few weeks in San Davers and appreciated the similarities and differences between working in a teaching hospital and a community hospital. Regardless of the setting, I know now <u>for sure</u> that using research-based nursing concepts and interventions is <u>without question</u> the way to quality care. It was nursing care that made the difference between life and death in the early months of the COVID-19 outbreak.

Especially in the hospital, it takes a team of respiratory therapists, physical therapists, physicians, and other ancillary clinical staff to heal. Sometimes one discipline takes the lead, sometimes another. Yet without nurses to coordinate the whole picture, patient care in a hospital isn't good enough. Jeez oh Pete, I sound like I'm writing a term paper.

These six months have taught me to appreciate how I process new information and compare it to what I thought were my values. For example, hearing the same thing over and over has had a real impact on what I believe. The news, advertisements, being socially alone, and being overly busy have all had me question the difference between logic and reality. Sometimes being told over and over that I am mistaken can make me believe alternate explanations. I have seen it in the hospital when we've been told nurses are heroes, and then almost simultaneously told we can't understand a patient care idea or that we've misremembered something. Remember when we were told we nurses did such a good job at not contracting COVID that we no longer needed adequate supplies of PPE? Then, when that assumption was questioned, we were told that the idea of protection and financial solvency was too complicated for us to understand.

Without question, it would be so easy for somebody like me to believe this stuff. I'm especially vulnerable to the advice given by authority figures, especially if it begins with a compliment. I know it's called gaslighting, but it's hard to resist. It has made me feel lost. What's true and what's false? Why does everyone seem to have an answer except me?

There is still a lot that is not known about treating and restraining the spread of COVID-19. I need to be OK with that unknown.

I need to also remind myself that my work life isn't my whole life. I can't foresee what will happen to my family throughout this plague. I don't know if it's safe for Gram to participate in vaccine trials. I'm not as concerned about Mark, haha. I don't know if Tala will run away from COVID-19 and join the Sisters of Angels and Cherubim. What would I do if Tala becomes a SAC? Who would teach me how to attack nursing injustices and use inventive expressions to blow off steam?

Thank goodness I've got Gram, Harrison, Tala, and Dad to remind me that multiple sources of information are not my enemy. I wrote down what they've said to me so that I can come back and remind myself that I need other people who aren't just an echo chamber.

Gram: There's a limit to what any of us can know. Keep a balance, Kit. Bake, walk, read...just be creative. Creativity helps the mind sort out big information.

Dad: Be tolerant of not knowing. I don't mean ignoring information but accepting different perspectives. I know you like to make lists and I know you used to love to web search for hours. Your curiosity is a gift. So, do what you do well. Make a list of what you hear, and then see what's online and in the news. Then, evaluate who is talking and what they're saying. Are they experts? Is there only one point of view? I can't promise you the truth with a capital T, but maybe don't worry as much about what you don't know. Keep talking to me and your whole family.

Tala: People are lifesaving ropes. Other people help us know and appreciate the world and all its unstopping confusion. People are God's messengers. Trust those who you know have your best interests at heart. My dad was a big believer in helping others and listening to trusted friends. He told me this Indian proverb: "A person who would do great things should not attempt them all alone." Here is a Tala proverb: "If someone is telling you something that sounds like bull pucky, then consider it exactly that until proven otherwise."

Harrison: Just admit you're lost. I get lost a lot! When I admit it, I'm more aware. When I'm more aware, I'm more hopeful because even if the thing seems awful, at least it's got a name. I can fight something with a name. Just because we've never been down this road before doesn't mean we'll be lost forever. Let's be lost together, my Kit. We can figure this out. I'm optimistic we will be found.

So, even though there won't be a family cookout today, I'm going to do my best to be OK with the mystery of COVID-19. I'll *read, listen, and stay in touch with my people. I'll create something delicious to take to work tonight to share.*

Thankfully, my head is still above water. Confused and feeling lost sometimes but paddling like crazy below the surface. Until the answers eventually become apparent, I'll keep making my way back to normal.

The End

Thank you for reading Kit Wilson, RN: Treading Water.

I hope you've enjoyed reading a little bit about what it was like to be a hospital nurse in early 2020. The stories were meant to shed some light on a tough time in our world's history. I hope you have a better understanding of what the situation was like in hospitals and in one nurse's personal life. You know, context.

I think my colleagues and I coped pretty well with the first few months of COVID-19 considering the slap in the face the pandemic dealt to personal lives. And to the U.S. health care system.

In the second half of 2020, there were peaks and valleys in the outbreak. Cases would fall and then rise again. Medical treatments enjoyed more success and gained stronger acceptance. We got out of our homes and relished time with others again. Some businesses were able to reopen.

The best news was the emergency approval and release of COVID-19 vaccines.

I have some more stories to tell you. These stories are about courage, tragedy, kindness, and malevolence. They're told through the eyes of a more experienced (thanks to my patients and colleagues), family-loving (missed hugging you guys), sassier (thanks Tala), and more open to romance (looking at you, Harrison) registered nurse.

These stories will tell you I and my favorite cast of characters: Mom, Dad, Maddy, Mandy, Teddy, Kai, Linda, Little Mark, Erin, Mary, Tala, and Harrison learned to live with COVID craziness. I hope you can join us.

<u>Stay safe.</u>
<u>Coming in 2023</u>: *Kit Wilson, RN: Re-Creating Normal*

References and Credit Notes:

Chapter 12 epigraph:
> *https://www.cnr.ncsu.edu/news/2020/05/coronavirus-toilet-paper-shortage/*

Chapter 13 epigraph:
> *https://www.census.gov/library/stories/2021/09/pandemic-disrupts-some-trends-in-health-care-services*

Chapter 19
> Penn Proning Guidelines, University of Pennsylvania, Philadelphia PA *https://www.pennmedicine.org/updates/blogs/penn-physician-blog/2020/may/proning-during-COVID-19*
>
> Proning COVID-19 Patients Reduces Need for Ventilators. https://www.cuimc.columbia.edu/news/proning-COVID19-patients-reduces-need-ventilators

Chapter 26

1. I Want a Hippopotamus for Christmas " song written by John Rox (1902–1957) and performed by Gayla Peevey in 1953.

Chapter 28
Headline References

1. Use of a social bubble
   "If managed appropriately, social bubbles can be an effective way of extending contacts beyond the household while limiting the increase in epidemic risk"
   https://www.ajmc.com/view/a-timeline-of-COVID19-developments-in-2020https://pubmed.ncbi.nlm.nih.gov/33623826/

2. COVID deaths:
   "Deaths across America spiked as Covid-19 began its spread...researchers reported Monday. "Notable increases" in deaths were seen in March and early April, the team led by the Yale School of Public Health found"
   https://www.cnn.com/2020/04/27/health/deaths-spike-COVID-spread/index.html

3. Pope Francis Easter message:
   "Pope Francis called for the world to be united in the face of Covid-19 as he delivers Easter message from an empty St. Peter's Cathedral in Rome"
   https://www.npr.org/2020/04/12/832833507/pope-francis-praises-the-contagion-of-hope-in-easter-message#

4. Unemployment in early COVID:
   "A decade-long economic expansion ended March 2020 due to Covid-19 with businesses closing or suspending operations. The economic expansion, which continued for 128 months or 42 quarters,

was the longest economic expansion on record until millions of jobs were lost because of the pandemic"

https://www.bls.gov/opub/mir/2021/article/unem-ployment-rises-in-2020-as-the-country-battles-the-COVID-19-pandemic.htm

5. U.S. strategic stockpile:
   "The U.S. Strategic National Stockpile is almost depleted amid widespread shortages of medical equip-ment to fight Covid"

   https://www.cnn.com/world/live-news/coronavirus-pandemic-04-01-20-

6. Vaccine:
   "How long will a vaccine really take? A vaccine would be the ultimate weapon against the coronavirus and the best route back to normal life"

   https://www.nytimes.com/interactive/2020/04/30/opinion/coronavirus-COVID-vaccine.html

7. Teachers working online:
   "In the last semester, teachers all over the state have had to figure out how to keep kids from fall-ing behind when they're unable to meet with their pupils every day in the classroom. While some have an easier time than others, whether due to avail-able technology or the ages of their students, sev-eral teachers agree on one thing: they want to be back in school."

   https://dailystandard.com/archive/2020-05-05/stories/40410/teachers-adapt-to-new-normal

8. High school seniors in early 2020 during COVID: *"Class of 2020 high school seniors reflect on Covid-19 and missed milestones"*

https://www.ktvb.com/article/news/health/coronavirus/hig-school-seniors-class-2020-graduates-graduation-prom-ceremony-corona-virus-COVID19/277-48baac60-a014-4c1c-86ba-50f2be7f87c8

Chapter 40

1. COVID cases on the decline:

https://www.washingtonpost.com/nation/2020/08/20

About the Author

Beth E. Heinzeroth White graduated from a hospital-based diploma school of nursing. She went on to earn Bachelor of Science in Nursing and Master of Science in Nursing degrees. Her career has spanned adult critical care to nursing care of children and perinatal nursing care. She has taught nursing of children and nursing management courses in diploma, ASN, and BSN programs. Beth's clinical practice as a certified Pediatric Clinical Nurse Specialist centered on her particular interests in pediatric palliative care and developmental pediatrics, particularly care of children with spina bifida. She is the co-author of two award-winning books: *In the Shadows: How to Care for Your Seriously Ill Adult Child* (2013: Hygeia Press), awarded the 2013 AJN Book of the Year in the Consumer Health category, and *Caps, Capes and Caring: The Legacy of Diploma Nursing Schools in Toledo* (2018: University of Toledo Press), awarded the Bowling Green State University Libraries CAC 2018 Local History Publication Award in the Independent Scholar category. Her debut novel was published in May 2022 and is the first in the Kit Wilson, RN series: *Kit Wilson, RN: First Year Nurse.* She is semi-retired and lives in northwest Ohio.

Made in USA - Kendallville, IN
76019_9781735934723
03.27.2023 1327